1981                                        2001

# *Reagan, Bush, & Clinton*

## ROURKE'S COMPLETE HISTORY OF OUR PRESIDENTS ENCYCLOPEDIA

*Volume 12*

### Kelli L. Hicks

Ypsilanti District Library
5577 Whittaker Road
Ypsilanti, MI 48197

**RoURKE PUBLISHING**

Vero Beach, Florida 32964 | www.rourkepublishing.com

© 2009 Rourke Publishing LLC

All rights reserved. No part of this book may be reproduced or utilized in any form or by any means, electronic or mechanical including photocopying, recording, or by any information storage and retrieval system without permission in writing from the publisher.

www.rourkepublishing.com

PHOTO CREDITS: Pages 4, 5, 11, 12, 13, 14, 15, 16, 18, 20, 21: Courtesy of Ronald Reagan Presidential Library ; Page 6: Zoltán Pataki, Darren Hendley, James Steidl; Page 7: Carmen Martinez; Page 8: Gary Woodard, Kevin Russ; Pages 9, 10, 19, 22, 34, 39, 53: Wikipedia; Pages 23, 24, 25, 26, 27, 28, 29, 30, 31, 32, 33: George H.W. Bush Presidential Library and Museum; Pages 35, 36, 37, 38, 40, 43, 44, 45, 46, 48, 49, 50, 51, 52: Courtesy of William J. Clinton Presidential Library

Editor: Kelli L. Hicks

Cover and interior design by Nicola Stratford, bdpublishing.com

### Library of Congress Cataloging-in-Publication Data

Rourke's Complete History of Our Presidents Encyclopedia / Kelli L. Hicks
  p. cm.
Includes bibliographical references and index.
  Summary: Discusses the political lives and times of the men who served as United States presidents, their administrations, and the events which occurred during their tenures.
  Set ISBN 978-1-60694-293-2
  Title ISBN 978-1-60694-305-2
  1. Presidents—United States—Juvenile literature.

Printed in the USA
CG/CG

www.rourkepublishing.com – rourke@rourkepublishing.com
Post Office Box 3328, Vero Beach, FL 32964

*The 1980s and 1990s* ...............................4

*Ronald W. Reagan (1981-1989)* ...................10

*George H. W. Bush (1989-1993)* ...................22

*William J. Clinton (1993-2001)* ....................34

*Looking Back, and Forward* ........................54

*Cabinet Members* ................................55

*Timeline* ........................................56

*Presidents of the United States* ....................60

*Index* ..........................................62

*Further Reading* .................................64

# The 1980s and 1990s

In the late 1970s, President Jimmy Carter had a particularly tough job: He had to get Americans to understand that there were limits. There were limits on how much power the United States had in the world and limits on the amount of resources Americans could consume. During the presidential campaign of 1980, Carter's Republican opponent, Ronald Reagan, disagreed. He told Americans that their troubles were over; that there was nothing but clear sailing ahead.

Apparently, that was what Americans wanted to hear. On November 4, 1980, they elected Ronald Reagan by a landslide, and thus began a decade that would become associated with greed and lavish displays of wealth. Reagan's Washington, D.C., inauguration celebrations in January 1981 set the lush tone.

The festivities cost the taxpayers 8 million dollars. First Lady Nancy Reagan's ball gown alone was worth thousands.

While most Americans could not afford clothes that expensive in the 1980s, many nonetheless, would pay quite a lot for items with designer labels. Jeans sporting the name of a famous designer, and a hefty price tag, gained enormous popularity in the 1980s. Meanwhile, ambitious young businesspeople, sometimes referred to as yuppies (young urban professionals), were power-dressing, wearing clothes that trumpeted their intent to climb the ladder of success.

*President Reagan and his wife Nancy pose in the White House Red Room prior to an Inaugural Ball in Washington, D.C.*

*President Reagan and the First Lady, who both enjoyed entertaining, wait at the North portico of the White House to receive their guests, the Prime Minister of Australia and his wife.*

# The 1980s and 1990s

# 6   The 1980s and 1990s

A cable television channel called MTV (Music Television) featured music videos, some of which depicted sexual themes, drug use, and violence. Talk shows on which people discussed their most intimate secrets and problems tried to outdo one another with outrageousness.

*The Video Home System (VHS), developed in Japan, was introduced to the United States in 1977.*

Videocassette recorders were among the fastest-selling appliances in the 1980s. In 1982, about 3 percent of American homes had at least one; by 1988, almost 60 percent did. Americans could now tape television programs and rent movies on video to watch whenever they liked.

That flexibility, combined with more program offerings via cable television, gave Americans virtually limitless opportunities to become couch potatoes.

The evolving video culture became progressively more uninhibited. Some television programs displayed a frankness and crudeness that viewers and censors would have rejected just a few years earlier.

*Americans in the 1950s looked to television as their primary source for news and information.*

## The 1980s and 1990s

Sixty-one percent of U.S. homes had microwave ovens by the end of the 1980s. Speeding up food preparation went right along with the life-in-the-fast-lane lifestyle of many Americans. More and more people bought personal computers, and for many, the distinction between work time and personal time became increasingly blurred.

After a dramatic fall in the stock market in October 1987 and the arrest of a number of businesspeople whose ambitions and greed had led them to break the law, the allure of the money-chasing lifestyle seemed to wear off a little.

In January 1989, President George Bush tried to steer a new course with his inaugural speech. "My friends," he said, "we are not the sum of our possessions. In our hearts we know what matters. We cannot hope only to leave our children a bigger car, a bigger bank account. We must hope to give them a sense of what it means to be a loyal friend, a loving parent, a citizen who leaves his home, his neighborhood and town a little better than he found it."

There were some serious problems largely ignored by the government during the 1980s, but the problems did not go away. Safety improvements in the nuclear power industry experienced extreme neglect, for example; now they would cost a great deal of time and money to implement. Hundreds of billions of taxpayer dollars would also have to be spent to correct losses resulting from lax banking and business practices allowed during the Reagan administration.

*The Nec Corporation developed the first mass-produced laptop in 1986 with a 2,560 kbps modem.*

# 8  The 1980s and 1990s

Another serious social problem on the rise was homelessness. By 1990, estimates of the number of homeless people in America varied a great deal, with many figures nearing 3 million. The Reagan administration's cuts in funding for low-income housing and social-welfare programs were partially to blame.

*The red ribbon is a symbol to promote AIDS awareness and to show support for those stricken with the disease.*

Doctors identified a new and terrible disease, acquired immune deficiency syndrome, or AIDS, in 1981. In that year, only a handful of cases were identified. By 1993, over 100,000 cases in the United States were reported.

*A homeless man looks for food in a dumpster.*

## Words to Know

**AIDS** (AYDZ): An acronym for acquired immune deficiency syndrome; this disease impairs the human immune system to the point that the body cannot fight off serious infection or disease.

**middle class** (MID-uhl KLASS): This social group, made up of people who rank between the poor and the wealthy, includes professionals and business workers.

Homelessness increased through the early 1990s. When Congress passed and President Bill Clinton signed a welfare-reform act in August 1996, some people feared that even more Americans might be pushed into poverty and homelessness.

The cost of living was high, and pressures on middle-class families trying to make ends meet were often overwhelming. It was to these Americans who Democratic presidential candidate Bill Clinton appealed to most in 1992.

Brought up in a small town in one of the nation's poorer states, Clinton could communicate with working people, and he talked about wanting to make things better for them. This would not be easy to achieve.

In addition to social problems, President Clinton had to face a new and dangerous threat to U.S. citizens: terrorism. Throughout history, terrorist attacks on American soil were unusual and rare events. In the 1990s, however, there was a growing awareness among Americans that they could be the targets of terrorist acts.

On February 26, 1993, just a month after Clinton's inauguration as president, there was a terrible explosion in New York City's World Trade Center. The explosion killed six people and injured more than 1,000 when a bomb went off in a van that had been parked in a garage under the huge building.

On April 19, 1995, the terrorist target was a federal building in Oklahoma City, Oklahoma. That bombing killed 166 people, 19 of them innocent children.

On July 27, 1996, during the Olympic Games held in Atlanta, Georgia, a bomb went off at an outdoor park, killing a woman, contributing to the fatal heart attack of a journalist, and wounding more than 100 people.

President Clinton asked Congress to pass stricter laws to fight terrorism. In signing such a law on August 5, 1996, he called terrorism the enemy of our generation.

*A terrorist attack on the Alfred P. Murrah Federal Building in Oklahoma City, Oklahoma, was heard and felt up to 55 miles (89km) away.*

Whether or not Clinton had succeeded in improving life for Americans was a factor in the outcome of the election of 1996, when he ran for reelection against Republican Bob Dole. Another factor was the approach of the twenty-first century. Which candidate did the voters think would be best for America in the new era? On November 5, 1996, Americans went to the polls to make that decision.

# Ronald Reagan

The man preparing to face the television cameras was a veteran Hollywood actor. He was 69 years old, but looked considerably younger, the result of many years of careful attention to his appearance. As makeup artists and hairdressers completed their work, the man stepped forward, but not to perform in a movie.

Ronald Reagan was preparing, on this day in October 1980, for a presidential debate. An actor-turned-politician, Reagan was seeking what he would later call the greatest role of his life, the presidency of the United States.

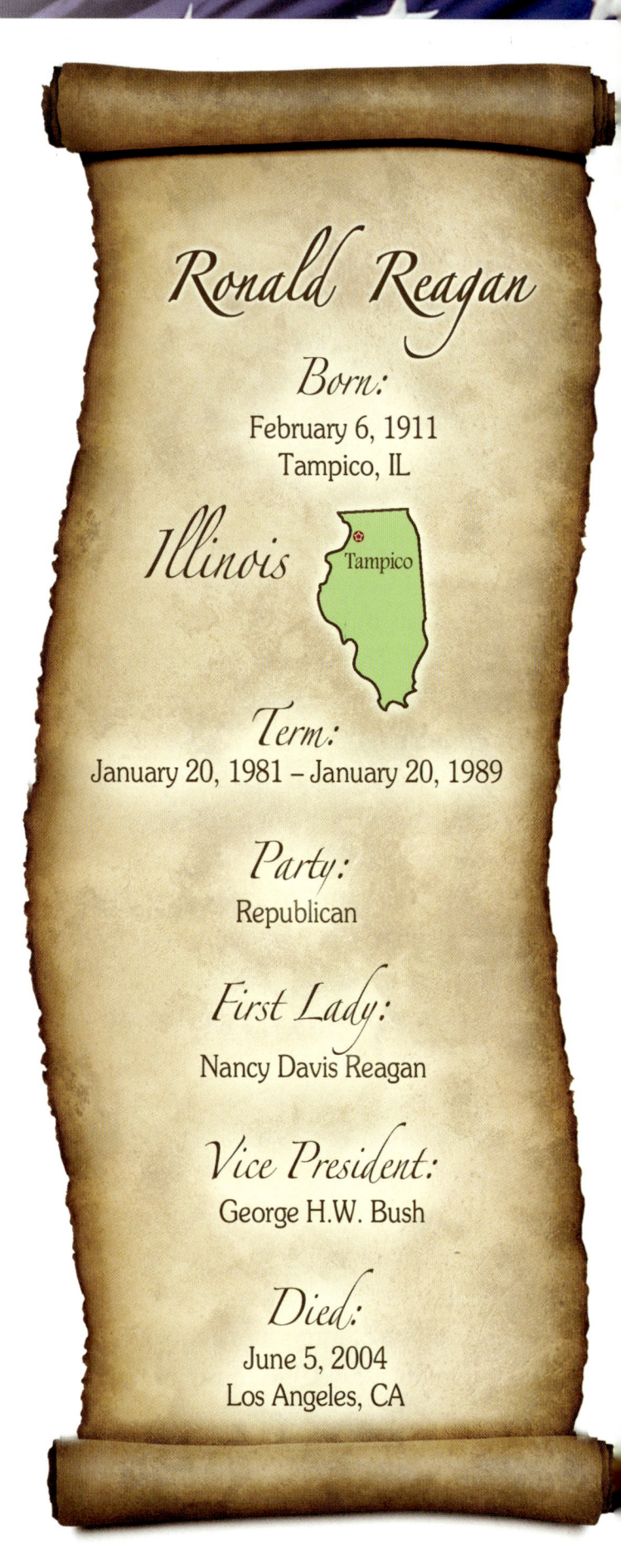

*Vice President George H.W. Bush*

### Ronald Reagan

**Born:**
February 6, 1911
Tampico, IL

*Illinois* — Tampico

**Term:**
January 20, 1981 – January 20, 1989

**Party:**
Republican

**First Lady:**
Nancy Davis Reagan

**Vice President:**
George H.W. Bush

**Died:**
June 5, 2004
Los Angeles, CA

# Ronald Reagan

**40th President of the United States**

# Ronald Reagan

## The Early Years

Ronald Wilson Reagan was born on February 6, 1911, in the small Illinois town of Tampico. The Reagan family, Jack and Nelle and their sons Neil and Ronald, did not have much money.

However, the boys' greatest pleasures; sledding, ice skating, and playing football, cost nothing. When Ronald was nine, the family moved to Dixon, Illinois.

As a young man, Reagan attended Eureka College, near his Dixon home. A football scholarship and jobs waiting tables and washing dishes helped pay his way. He graduated in June 1932, at the height of the Great Depression, the most serious economic crisis in American history.

*Reagan worked as a sports radio announcer at WHO Radio in Des Moines, Iowa from 1934-1937.*

Reagan was thus very fortunate to get a job as a radio sports announcer in Davenport, Iowa. He hoped that it would lead to a break into show business. Eventually, it did. While covering the Chicago Cubs, a baseball team, during spring training in California, Reagan managed to get both an agent and a screen test.

He landed a contract with Warner Brothers, one of the major movie studios. From the late 1930s to the early 1950s, he performed as a star in many low-budget movies.

*Ronald Reagan at the age of 23, in 1934.*

# Ronald Reagan

*Reagan played George "The Gipper" Gipp in the film* Knute Rockney, All American *in 1940.*

*Newlyweds Ronald and Nancy Reagan cut their wedding cake at best man William Holden's house in Toluca, California on March 4, 1952.*

In 1940, he married an actress named Jane Wyman. In 1941, they had a daughter, Maureen, and four years later, they adopted a baby boy named Michael.

During World War II, Reagan served in the army, for the most part making training movies. When he returned to civilian life, Reagan became very involved in the Screen Actors Guild, an actors' union. As its president, he fought against Communist influences in Hollywood. His marriage grew strained, and in June 1948, the couple divorced. Jane Wyman received custody of their children.

Soon afterward, Reagan met an actress named Nancy Davis. They were married on March 4, 1952. They had a daughter, Patti, and a son, Ronald Prescott, known as Ron, Jr.

## Words to Know

**inflation** (in-FLAY-shuhn): A sharp and continuous rise in prices.

## Reagan Enters Politics

During the 1950s, Reagan's interest in politics grew. As a Democrat, he worked on the presidential campaign of Dwight D. Eisenhower in 1952 and 1956. By 1962, however, he formally joined the Republican Party after working on Richard Nixon's campaign. In 1966, he won the election to be governor of California. The voters reelected him in 1970.

He watched from the sidelines in August 1974 as President Nixon resigned and Vice President Gerald Ford became president. In 1976, he challenged Ford for the Republican nomination. Ford very narrowly won the nomination in August, but lost the general election to Democrat Jimmy Carter in November.

Carter's four years in office were difficult, to say the least. Economic problems, including inflation and unemployment, affected many Americans. Fuel shortages led to long lines at gas stations and higher heating bills.

When 54 Americans were held hostage at the U.S. Embassy in Iran, Carter was unable to secure their release.

Americans were frustrated. They wanted a president who could take charge of things and make them feel good again. Reagan seemed to be their man. "There are those in our land," he said, "who would have us believe that the United States… has reached the zenith of its power. I don't

*Ronald Reagan addresses the crowd at the Governor's Inaugural Ball in Sacramento, California after being elected in 1966.*

believe that." He took a more optimistic view, declaring, "It's morning again in America." He swept through the Republican primaries and defeated his strongest opponent, George H.W. Bush, a former congressman from Texas.

In July 1980, delegates to the Republican Convention nominated Ronald Reagan for president, and Reagan chose Bush as his running mate.

The Democrats nominated President Carter at their convention and poked fun at Reagan's acting background. But Reagan's experience before cameras and microphones gave him a poise and a sense of timing that came across very well on television. He soon earned the nickname, the Great Communicator. During a televised debate less than a week before the election, Reagan looked calmly into the cameras and asked Americans, "Are you better off than you were four years ago?"

## The Presidency

In the November 1980 election, Reagan defeated both Jimmy Carter and Congressman John Anderson, a representative from Illinois who was running as an Independent candidate. After the results were in, Reagan, the oldest man ever elected U.S. president, announced, "We're going to put Americans back to work again." It would not be easy, however. The Democrats in Congress were prepared to fight many of Reagan's economic proposals.

On March 30, 1981, a man named John Hinckley, Jr., fired six shots at the president outside a Washington, D.C., hotel. A police officer, a Secret Service agent, and the White House press secretary were struck, and so was the president. A bullet entered the left side of his body and lodged in his lung, an inch away from his heart.

Secret Service agents rushed Reagan to a nearby hospital, where doctors performed emergency surgery to remove the bullet. "Honey, I forgot to duck," he told his wife, Nancy, when she quickly made her way to his side at the hospital. "I hope you're a Republican," he joked with one of the doctors. Reagan's poise under such circumstances made him a hero to many Americans.

*Reagan waves to the crowd outside the Washington Hilton Hotel on March 30, 1981, just before John Hinckley Jr., fired shots at the president in an assassination attempt.*

## First Lady Nancy Reagan

Nancy Reagan was born July 6, 1921, in New York City. Her parents, Ken and Edith Robbins, named her Anne Frances, but most people called her Nancy. Her father left her mother shortly after Nancy was born, and because her mother worked as a stage actress, Nancy spent most of her early years in the care of an aunt and an uncle. When her mother married a man named Dr. Loyal Davis in 1929, Nancy went to live with them in Chicago. In 1937, her family officially changed her name to Nancy Davis.

After attending Smith College in Northampton, Massachusetts, she followed her mother's lead and pursued a career as an actress. In Hollywood, she fell in love with, and married, the actor Ronald Reagan. When her husband entered politics, she enjoyed her role as his supporter and mother of their children, Patti and Ron, Jr.

Nancy Reagan had expensive taste, and that often got her in trouble with the taxpaying public after Reagan became president. The First Lady spent over $900,000 on remodeling the White House and $220,000 on a set of china in her favorite color of red, at a time when funding for many programs for the poor were being cut. She also received much criticism for having too much influence on presidential decisions.

Mrs. Reagan became more popular with the public when she became active in the fight against drug abuse, becoming a spokesperson for the Just Say No campaign. Her strong-willed devotion and loyalty to her husband as president has made her an enduring figure in U.S. politics.

---

Many applauded the president for his appointment of Sandra Day O'Connor as the nation's first woman Supreme Court justice. He also received a lot of public support, as well as criticism, for his tough response to a strike by the nation's air-traffic controllers.

As government employees, they were not supposed to strike. "The law is the law, and the law says they cannot strike," he said, and he fired those who would not return to work.

Reagan promoted an economic policy that analysts called supply-side, or trickle-down, economics.

According to this economic theory, tax cuts for the wealthy would supply them with more money, and the benefits of their spending would trickle down to those less well-off. Americans were fiercely divided on the advisability of this policy. Reagan was also in favor of cutting federal-government spending on a number of social-welfare programs while at the same time greatly increasing military spending. Together, these policies received the title of Reaganomics.

While many people applauded these policies, others thought they were dangerous. Their implementation resulted in the federal government spending much more money than it took in. When this happens, the difference between income and spending is known as a budget deficit. The budget deficit, which was 74 billion dollars when Reagan took the oath of office, rose to about 128 billion dollars in 1982 and 208 billion dollars in 1983.

Problems also resulted from Reagan's policy of deregulation. This reduced governmental control over certain industries, such as airlines and savings and loan (S&L) institutions. Critics' warnings that such powerful industries needed greater regulation, not less, seemed silly to many Americans in the fast-lane 1980s.

However, as the decade wore on, safety concerns emerged in the airline industry, and massive abuses and fraud surfaced in the S&L industry, costing Americans billions of dollars and proving that the critics had been concerned with good reason.

Dismal foreign problems continued to haunt the nation as well. In 1982, U.S. Marines went to Lebanon in an effort to stabilize that country, which was being torn apart by a civil war. On October 23, 1983, a terrorist drove a truck filled with explosives into a building where American troops were sleeping killing 241 marines.

Two days later, on October 25, the U.S. sent marines to Grenada, a tiny island nation in the Caribbean. Eighteen American soldiers died during the evacuation of some 1,100 U.S. citizens and students, who many believed were under the threat of a tense political situation there.

## Words to Know

**Reaganomics** (ray-guhn-OM-iks): The economic policies advanced during the administration of Ronald Reagan, specifically, supply-side, or trickle-down, theory. This theory supposes that tax breaks and other incentives for the wealthy will boost the economy, the benefits of which will trickle down to others. Reaganomics also included cuts in social-welfare spending and increases in military spending.

*President Reagan is sworn into office in the Rotunda at the U.S. Capitol to begin his second term on January 20, 1985.*

Reagan's greatest fear was the spread of Communism, and he called the Soviet Union the Evil Empire. He wanted the U.S. military to build the Strategic Defense Initiative, which would use satellites in space to shoot down incoming nuclear missiles. This program, which reportedly would cost trillions of dollars, became known as Star Wars.

## A Second Term

By 1984, it was obvious that Reagan would run for reelection. The economy seemed to be prospering, and he was so personally popular that many people were willing to overlook the serious problems still facing the United States.

The Democrats nominated Walter Mondale, who served as vice president under Jimmy Carter, to run against Reagan. When Mondale asked New York congresswoman Geraldine Ferraro to be his running mate, the Democrats became the first major political party ever to choose a woman for the vice-presidential spot.

Reagan won a dramatic victory on November 6, 1984, gaining 59 percent of the popular vote and 525 electoral votes. Mondale won the electoral votes of only his home state of Minnesota and the District of Columbia. Speaker of the House Thomas "Tip" O'Neill, a Democrat, described Reagan as the most popular figure in the history of the United States.

### Words to Know

**Electoral College** (i-LEKT-or-uhl KOL-ij): The group that formally elects the president and vice president by casting electoral votes, members of the Electoral College are elected by popular vote, the vote of the people, in each state.

On July 13, 1985, Reagan, then 74 years old, underwent surgery to remove a cancerous tumor from his large intestine. He recovered quickly and returned to work.

During his second term, President Reagan carried on a war against terrorism. He blamed the leader of Libya, Muammar al-Qaddafi, whom he called the mad dog of the Middle East, for supporting terrorists. When a U.S. serviceman in a German nightclub died in a bomb explosion that had links to Qaddafi, Reagan ordered a swift reprisal. On April 14, 1986, U.S. fighter-bombers struck the Libyan cities of Tripoli and Benghazi.

In November 1986, a scandal erupted. News leaked of secret sales of American military supplies to Iran, made in return for Iran's influence on terrorists holding U.S. citizens hostage in Lebanon. News of this arms-for-hostages deal was very badly received, because it meant that the Reagan administration was negotiating with terrorists, something it had vowed never to do.

To make matters worse, profits from these arms sales were being used, again secretly, to supply aid to rebels in Nicaragua. Throughout his presidency, Reagan had been concerned about the Central American country of Nicaragua, where rebels, called Contras were fighting the Communist government. Reagan had sent a great deal of aid to the Contras.

*At the end of the Iran-Contra hostage crisis, Vice President George H.W. Bush and other VIPs wait to welcome hostages home.*

But in 1984, Congress passed the Boland Amendment, which banned further aid. It seemed that, despite the ban, the Reagan administration had continued to aid the Contras.

The Iran-Contra scandal, as the secret operation was soon called, became the subject of a major congressional investigation. It turned out that a National Security Council staff member, Marine Lieutenant Colonel Oliver North, had been running the secret operation.

He claimed that he was following orders and testified before a congressional committee that "I assumed that the President was aware of what I was doing and had, through my superiors, approved it."

Several of Reagan's key advisors resigned because of the scandal. People everywhere wondered how involved the president had been. Reagan claimed that he did not know about any funding for the Contras, but many people found this hard to believe.

Although his typical management style of leaving details to his subordinates made it possible that this statement was true, that very fact led people to question a president who did not know what was going on within his administration.

During Reagan's second term, he met several times with Soviet leader Mikhail Gorbachev to discuss nuclear arms control. In 1987, the two leaders signed the Intermediate-Range Nuclear Forces (INF) Treaty, which called for the destruction of many nuclear missiles. Many considered it quite an accomplishment for such an anti-Communist figure as Reagan to be making peace with the Soviet Union.

*President Reagan believed that if he worked at diplomacy with Soviet Secretary General Gorbachev, that the Soviets would be open to democracy and it could end Communism.*

# Ronald Reagan

*President Reagan salutes America as he boards the helicopter at the U.S. Capitol on his last day in office on January 20, 1989.*

## After the Presidency

As Reagan's presidency drew to a close, his vice president, George Bush, defeated the Democratic candidate, Michael Dukakis, and won the election. On January 20, 1989, Reagan was pleased to hand over the reins of power to Bush and move with Nancy back to California, to a home that wealthy supporters purchased for them. Frequent visits to his nearby ranch and writing his memoirs kept him busy for some time.

On November 5, 1994, Ronald Reagan revealed that he had been diagnosed with Alzheimer's disease, the main symptoms of which include memory loss, mental disorientation and gradually diminishing physical health.

Reagan reported that he had been experiencing symptoms for about a year. He declared, "I have begun the journey that will lead me into the sunset of my life." He said that he had made his condition public to increase awareness of the disease. As the disease progressed, his wife Nancy limited Reagan's contact with the public because she felt that "Ronnie would want people to remember him as he was," before Alzheimer's, took control of his body and mind. Ronald Reagan died in his Bel Air home on June 5, 2004, at the age of 93.

*President Reagan and Vice President George H.W. Bush, 1981*

# George H.W. Bush

On April 30, 1789, General George Washington placed his hand on a Bible and took the oath of office to become America's first president. On January 20, 1989, 200 years later, another man named George took the same oath of office. This man was George Bush, the 41st president of the United States.

## From Bomber Pilot to Businessman and Politician

George Herbert Walker Bush was born on June 12, 1924, in Milton, Massachusetts. His parents, Prescott and Dorothy Bush, moved the next year to prosperous Greenwich, Connecticut, where George grew up with his three brothers and one sister. It was Kennebunkport, Maine, however, where his family spent summers at their grandfather's home, that he would remember most fondly.

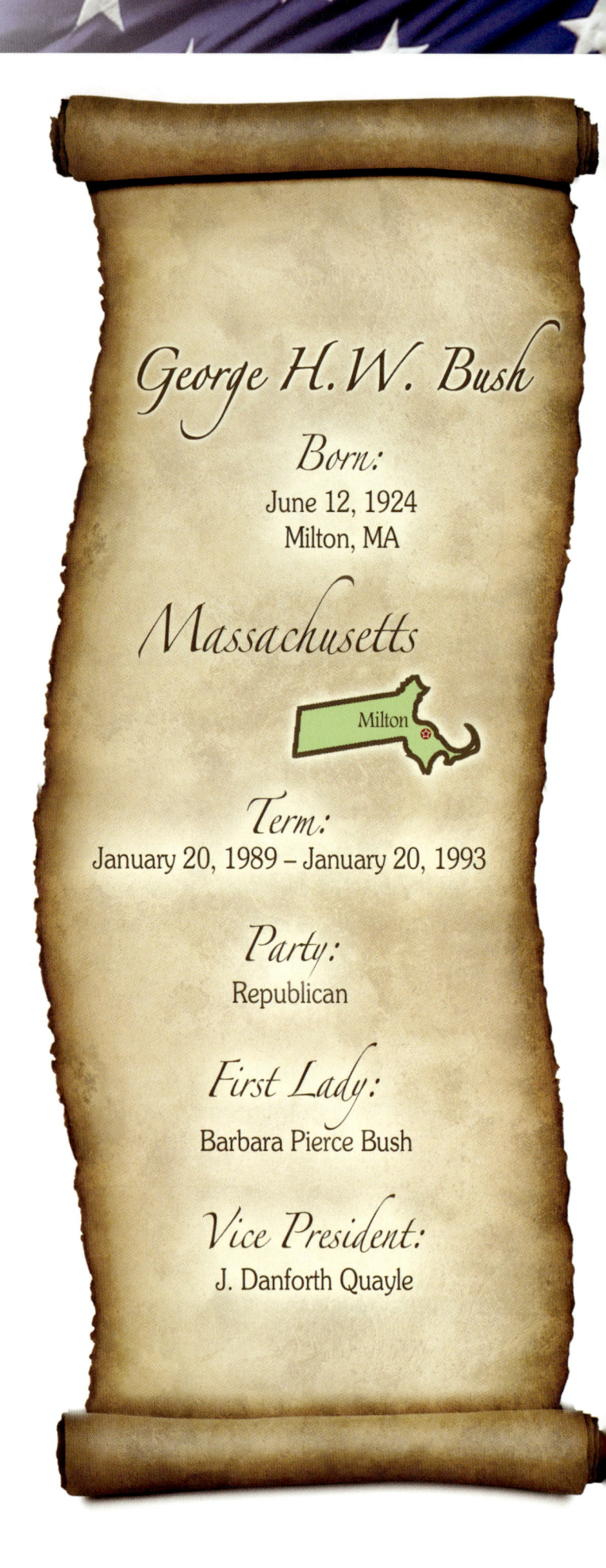

*Vice President J. Danforth Quayle*

---

*George H.W. Bush*

Born:
June 12, 1924
Milton, MA

*Massachusetts*

Term:
January 20, 1989 – January 20, 1993

Party:
Republican

First Lady:
Barbara Pierce Bush

Vice President:
J. Danforth Quayle

George H.W. Bush

41st President of the United States

# George H.W. Bush

*George and Barbara married in Rye, New York on January 6, 1945, only a few weeks after he returned from the war.*

*George H.W. Bush, a left-handed first baseman, was the captain of the baseball team that played in the first two College World Series.*

In June 1942, after he graduated from Phillips Academy, an exclusive prep school in Andover, Massachusetts, and turned 18, Bush enlisted in the U.S. Navy. It was the height of World War II, and by the following spring, he had earned an officer's commission and had become the youngest bomber pilot in the navy at that time. He survived being shot down off the coast of Japan on September 2, 1944. All together, Bush received three medals for bravery during the war.

On January 6, 1945, Bush married his sweetheart, Barbara Pierce. They moved to New Haven, Connecticut, when Bush entered Yale University. At Yale, he studied economics, played baseball, and became a father. His first child, George, Jr., was born there.

Bush graduated after only two and a half years, in the spring of 1948. The family then moved to Texas, where Bush began a very successful career in the oil business. Over the next few years, he and Barbara became the parents of five more children, although a daughter, Robin, died of leukemia at the age of three in 1953.

In the early 1960s, Bush turned to politics. He ran in 1964 for the U.S. Senate as a Republican in the largely Democratic state of Texas. Even though he lost, Bush was encouraged by how well he had done, and he admitted to a friend that he had been bitten by the political bug.

# George H.W. Bush

He won the election to the U.S. Congress in 1966 and others regarded him as a decent man who, although a conservative Republican, took a liberal stand on civil rights.

In 1970, Bush resigned from the House to run for the Senate again, but Democrat Lloyd Bentsen narrowly defeated him. He served as the U.S. ambassador to the United Nations until President Richard Nixon asked him to head the Republican National Committee. Soon afterward, Vice President Spiro Agnew was forced to resign, as was President Nixon.

Agnew faced charges of income tax evasion and the Watergate scandal plagued Nixon. Bush did his best to help both the new president, Gerald Ford, and the Republican Party weather the storm.

*Bush served as the Director of the CIA from 1976-1977.*

In September 1974, Bush went to China as head of the U.S. Liaison Office. In January 1976, he began another difficult challenge. He became head of the Central Intelligence Agency (CIA). An agency that, as Bush himself said had been "battered by a decade of hostile Congressional investigations, exposes, and charges that ran from lawbreaking to simple incompetence."

*Bush's victory in the Congressional race in 1966 made him the first Republican to represent Houston in the House of Representatives.*

## Words to Know

**liberal** (LIB-ur-uhl): In politics, someone who tends to support civil liberties, change and reform, and the use of government to improve social conditions.

# George H.W. Bush

Each week, Bush briefed President Ford on all kinds of information gathered from around the world. When Jimmy Carter, a Democrat, won the presidential election in November 1976, Bush resigned as director of the CIA and returned to Texas. There, with an eye on the difficulties the Carter administration was having, Bush decided to run for president in 1977.

Ronald Reagan, the popular former governor of California, was also running for the Republican nomination. Bush called Reagan's plan voodoo economics, but Reagan proved to be unbeatable.

In July 1980, at the Republican Convention in Detroit, Michigan, Ronald Reagan won the nomination as the Republican candidate. Reagan asked Bush to be his running mate. "I'd be honored, Governor," was Bush's reply. Reagan and Bush won in November by a landslide vote over the Democratic candidates, Jimmy Carter and Walter Mondale.

*Vice President Bush and President Reagan enjoy a Press Club Dinner on February 5, 1981.*

## From Vice President to President

On March 30, 1981, Vice President Bush sat on an airplane headed for Austin, Texas, where he was due to give a speech, when he received word that the president had been shot. As soon as his plane landed, Bush immediately had it refueled, then headed back to Washington, D.C.

*President Ronald Reagan and Vice President George Bush work in the Oval Office of the White House in July of 1984.*

As Reagan recovered from his injury, the vice president filled in to keep the executive office running. After Reagan returned to work in the Oval Office, Bush went back to traveling around the country and the world on behalf of the president. While serving as vice president, he visited more than 70 countries.

Reagan and Bush easily won renomination at the Republican Convention in August 1984, and they won reelection on November 6, 1984. In July 1985, the president faced another health crisis when doctors discovered a cancerous tumor on his intestine.

# George H.W. Bush

*Vice President Bush visited with American troops stationed in Nuremberg, Germany, on February 5, 1983.*

*President Ronald Reagan and Vice President George Bush, accompanied by wives Nancy and Barbara, join hands after the President endorses Bushes run for the Presidency during the President's dinner, Washington, D.C., on May 11, 1988.*

While the president underwent surgery, George Bush stepped in as acting president. And during Reagan's convalescence, Bush helped keep the wheels of government turning.

As the 1988 campaign season opened, Bush made it clear that he was going to run for the presidency. He seemed a much stronger candidate than any of the other Republicans who were interested. The two strongest Democratic contenders during the primaries were the governor of Massachusetts, Michael Dukakis, and an African American minister and leader of the Rainbow Coalition, Jesse Jackson.

In July, the Democrats nominated Michael Dukakis, who chose Texas Senator Lloyd Bentsen as his running mate. In August, the Republicans chose Bush and J. Danforth "Dan" Quayle to represent them. Quayle was a 41-year-old senator from Indiana.

*Vice President Bush debates his opponent Michael Dukakis during the presidential campaign of 1988.*

## Words to Know

**Rainbow Coalition** (RAYN-boh koh-uh-LISH-uhn): The Rainbow Coalition is the organization, started by Jesse Jackson, that represents many diverse groups of Americans from different religious, ethnic, and racial backgrounds.

# George H.W. Bush

Bush pledged not to fight the huge federal deficit by raising taxes, saying, "Read my lips. No new taxes." He also promised that, with him as president, America would be a "kinder, gentler nation." He then kicked off a mudslinging campaign, blaming taxes, pollution, and crime found in Massachusetts on Governor Dukakis. Bush argued that the Democratic candidate was too liberal.

On November 8, Bush won easily, receiving 426 electoral votes. Dukakis received 111. Only 50 percent of Americans eligible to vote, however, actually participated in the election. It was the lowest voter turnout in the United States since 1924.

When he became America's 41st president on January 20, 1989, George Bush said, "I do not fear what is ahead. For our problems are large, but our heart is larger. Our challenges are great, but our will is greater."

One of the great challenges that Bush faced was the federal budget deficit, which was over 150 billion dollars. Difficult choices needed to be made regarding how the government would, and would not, spend money, and how it would raise the money to spend. Bush invited Congress to help determine where spending cuts were appropriate.

*President Bush signs the Executive Order Ethics Package on April 12, 1989, in the Oval Office as C. Boyden Gray, the president's counsel looks on.*

Another economic problem was the bankruptcy of hundreds of savings and loan institutions across the country. If the government did not step in, tens of thousands of Americans would lose their life savings. On February 6, 1989, President Bush outlined his plan to save, or bail out, the S&Ls. Although it helped, it would cost American taxpayers billions of dollars.

At the same time, Bush wanted to support spending on education, child care, and social programs. How to do this without raising the deficit and still meeting his campaign promise of no new taxes, however, was a dilemma.

## Words to Know

**domestic** (duh-MESS-tik): In politics, domestic affairs are the issues that concern the home country, as opposed to foreign affairs.

**federal budget deficit** (FED-ur-uhl BUHJ-it DEF-uh-sit): When the national government spends more money than it takes in, it is operating on a deficit. In a deficit, the government has to take out loans and then repay the loans with interest.

**literacy** (LIT-ur-uh-see): The ability to read and write.

## First Lady Barbara Bush

Barbara Pierce was born on June 8, 1925, and grew up in Rye, New York. At the age of 16, Barbara met a young man named George Bush at a Christmas dance. He was "the handsomest boy I'd ever seen," she recalled. While he served in the navy, Barbara attended Smith College in Northampton, Massachusetts. George and Barbara were married in Rye, New York, on January 6, 1945.

During their married life, the Bushes would live in 29 different homes while George pursued a career in business and public service. Barbara, meanwhile, cared for the children, George, Jr., Robin, Jeb, Neil, Marvin, and Dorothy.

When her husband became president, she immediately became a popular First Lady. With her white hair, devotion to her family, and sense of humor, she projected the image of a beloved grandmother.

A lifelong volunteer, Barbara Bush gave a great deal of her time and money to many causes. As First Lady, her two pet projects were leukemia research and literacy. She took the anguish of the memory of losing her three-year-old daughter, Robin, to leukemia in 1953 and put it to work helping children and their families suffering with this disease.

Her fight against illiteracy, she believed, was a fight against many other social problems. In March 1989, she established the Barbara Bush Foundation for Family Literacy. The former First Lady continued her work with this foundation and other volunteer projects after leaving the White House.

In June 1990, he felt no alternative than to reverse his policy and call for tax increases to deal with the deficit. Although this was an embarrassing moment for Bush, most people agreed that higher taxes were necessary to bring the runaway deficit under control.

Many observers felt that Bush was much stronger on foreign policy than on domestic matters. He enjoyed traveling and meeting with international leaders.

# George H.W. Bush

*President Bush meets with President Gorbachev of the Soviet Union in the East Room of the White House in 1990.*

He continued to cultivate relations with the Soviet Union, which had been improving since Mikhail Gorbachev had come to power in that country. After 40 tense years, the Cold War between the United States and the Soviet Union was coming to an end. With the breakup of the Soviet Union and the tearing down of the Berlin Wall, it looked like a New World Order, as Bush called it, was ready to be born.

Still, one Central American country, Panama, was creating problems for Bush. Its leader, Manuel Noriega, was believed to be heavily involved in drug trafficking. Bush first imposed economic penalties, or sanctions, against Panama and then ordered a military invasion in December 1989. Noriega was captured and brought to the United States, where he went to trial and was convicted, and imprisoned for his involvement in the drug trade.

The next summer, attention shifted to the Middle East. On August 2, 1990, the armed forces of Iraq invaded the tiny country of Kuwait, an important source of oil. President Bush and other world leaders feared that Iraq's leader, Saddam Hussein, might also attack Saudi Arabia and further endanger the world's oil supplies.

The United Nations set a deadline, January 15, 1991, for Iraq to withdraw its troops from Kuwait.

## Words to Know

**Cold War** (KOHLD WOR): The relationship between the Soviet Union and the United States for several decades after World War II, when a "war of words" substituted for what would have been a much more deadly war of weapons.

**sanctions** (SANGK-shuhnz): A government imposed penalty against another country or government, such as the refusal to sell certain items to them or to buy things from them, in the hope that these penalties will change something that the country or government is doing.

*President Bush gives a press conference to provide information about Iraq's invasion of Kuwait on August 8, 1990.*

A coalition of nations led by the United States began a huge military buildup in the Persian Gulf, and they placed tough economic sanctions on Iraq. Congress voted to authorize Bush to go to war against Iraq if necessary. Two days after the deadline had passed, Iraqi soldiers showed no sign of leaving Kuwait, and the coalition forces began bombing Iraq.

Operation Desert Storm, as the attack was code-named, was under the command of U.S. General Norman Schwarzkopf, whose actions were coordinated in Washington, D.C., by the chairman of the Joint Chiefs of Staff, Colin Powell. The ground attack on Iraqi forces began on February 23. Within four days, the Iraqi army was fleeing toward Baghdad and Kuwait received liberation. President Bush's approval rating in the polls soared to almost 90 percent. His reelection in 1992 seemed assured.

*George Bush meets with Saudi Arabian King Fahd to discuss the situation in Iraq.*

### Vice President J. Danforth Quayle

James Danforth Quayle III was born on February 4, 1947, in Indianapolis, Indiana. He grew up in a wealthy family and entered DePauw University in Indiana in 1965. After graduating in 1969, a family friend helped him to get a place in the Indiana National Guard, which allowed him to meet his national-service requirement under the draft law, but didn't put him in much danger of being sent to fight in the Vietnam War.

He married Marilyn Tucker on November 18, 1972, and eventually had three children. In 1974, Quayle graduated from law school, and two years later, won election to Congress as a Republican. In 1980, he became a senator, and soon established a reputation for being very conservative.

Presidential contender George Bush's choice of Dan Quayle as his running mate in 1988 came as a surprise to many. It also became controversial because of Quayle's use of family connections to get into the National Guard, especially considering his outspoken support of the war and the military. He appeared to be someone who used connections rather than personal achievements to get what he wanted, and many people found it hard to take him seriously.

When he spoke without notes, he often rambled and seemed confused. His reputation was not helped during the 1992 campaign by his criticism of a television character named Murphy Brown for having a baby without being married. After leaving the vice-presidency, he published three books including *vice-presidential memoirs* in 1994, and he spends his time working in business, writing a newspaper column, and making frequent public appearances and speeches.

---

During the next year, however, deep concern about the economy and a feeling among Americans that their leaders in Washington didn't really care about them diminished Bush's approval rating.

*Former President Jimmy Carter, former President George Bush, newly elected President Bill Clinton, and former President Gerald Ford*

As Bush sought reelection in 1992, he received criticism by ultra-conservatives in his own party, by the Independent candidate, Ross Perot, and by the Democrats. Although he won renomination at the Republican Convention, by November 1992, only about 36 percent of Americans polled approved of the job he was doing as president. "It's time for a change," Democratic candidate Bill Clinton said, and a majority of Americans agreed. On November 3, Bill Clinton won the presidential election.

## After the Presidency

After losing the presidency, Bush returned with his wife, Barbara, to Texas. There, they spent time visiting with their children and grandchildren. On April 27, 1994, Bush joined President Clinton and former presidents Gerald Ford, Jimmy Carter, and Ronald Reagan at Richard Nixon's funeral. In November 1994, he participated in a groundbreaking ceremony for the Bush Presidential Library in Texas.

As a private citizen, Bush has visited a number of foreign countries, including China in 1994 and Vietnam in 1995, to promote American government and business interests. In 1996, he spoke at the Republican National Convention in San Diego, California, in support of the Bob Dole-Jack Kemp ticket. Life for former president Bush, as for most former presidents, has remained a mixture of private business and public service.

### Words to Know

**conservative** (kuhn-SUR-vuh-tiv): In politics, a person who tends to oppose change and prefers the way things are or have been, and who usually supports a reduced role for government in people's lives is called conservative.

# William J. Clinton

On November 3, 1992, Americans went to the polls to elect a president. While most people would have considered the campaign over, the Democratic candidate, Bill Clinton, did not. He boarded several planes and staff ushered him in and out of cars. He appeared in nine different states that day, shaking hands, waving, and speaking to people until he literally had no voice left. His unofficial campaign theme song had been, *Don't Stop (Thinking About Tomorrow)*, and Bill Clinton could only wonder if tomorrow he would be the next president.

## A Boy from Hope

Bill Clinton was born in the small town of Hope, Arkansas, on August 19, 1946. His mother, Virginia, named him William Jefferson Blythe IV, after his father who had been killed in a car accident three months earlier.

*Vice President Al Gore*

---

*William J. Clinton*

**Born:**
August 19, 1946
Hope, AR

*Arkansas*

**Term:**
January 20, 1993 – January 20, 2001

**Party:**
Democrat

**First Lady:**
Hillary Rodham Clinton

**Vice President:**
Al Gore

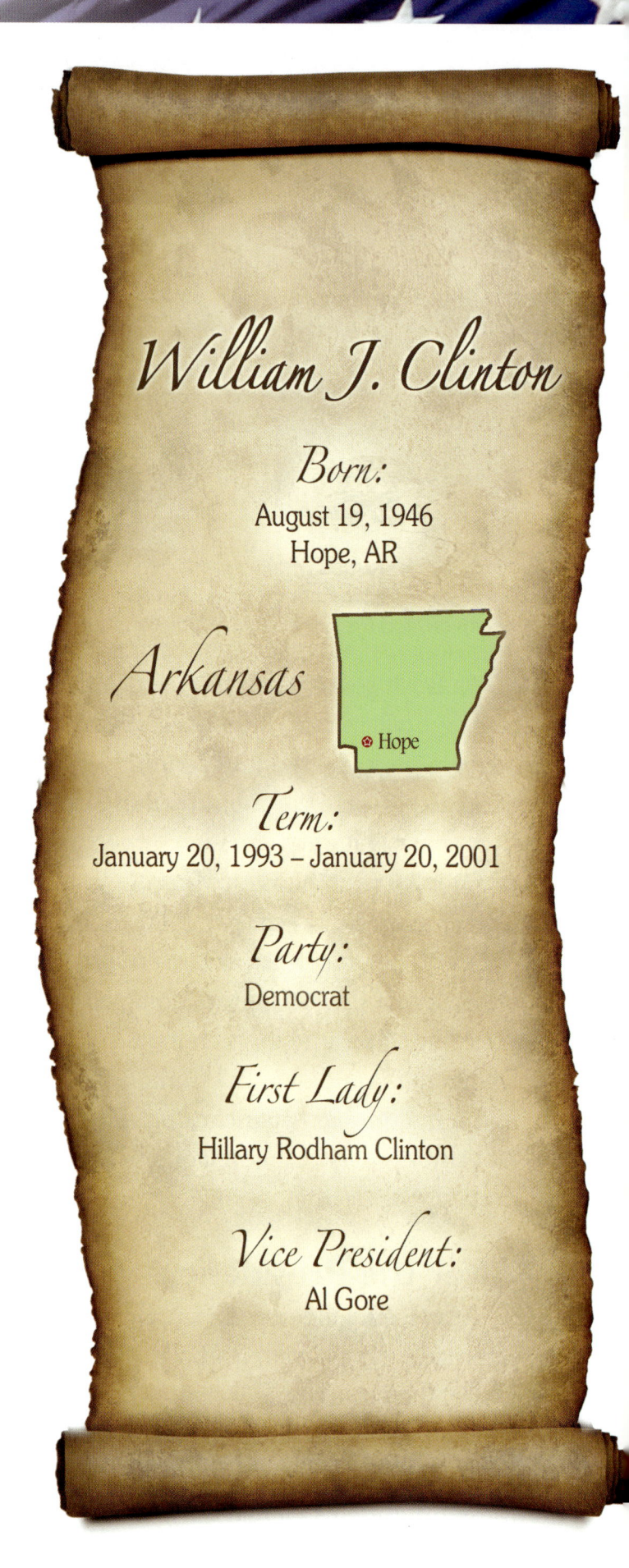

**William J. Clinton**

42nd President of the United States

# William J. Clinton

When Bill was almost two, his mother left him with her parents while she went to New Orleans to study nursing. His grandparents taught him to count, read, and most importantly, to treat people with kindness and respect, regardless of their race or economic status.

In 1950, his mother married a car salesman named Roger Clinton and the family moved to Hot Springs, Arkansas. When he was 15, Bill Blythe decided to take his stepfather's last name, Clinton. Bill was an excellent student, but his childhood was not an easy one. One evening after his abusive stepfather shot a gun inside the house, a teenage Bill Clinton confronted him. Taking his mother and younger brother Roger by the hands, Clinton said, "You will never hit either of them again. If you want them you'll have to go through me." The violence stopped.

## Boys Nation

Clinton had been interested in politics since watching the political conventions on television. When he was 16, Clinton traveled to Washington, D.C., with Boys Nation, a program that teaches about the workings of government. On this trip, he met President Kennedy and shook his hand.

In an interview near the end of his second term, Clinton recalled shaking hands with President Kennedy and how the experience helped him imagine the life he knew he wanted. During his own presidency, Clinton continued the tradition, meeting with the delegates of Boys Nation and Girls Nation each year.

*President Jimmy Carter greets the young and hopeful Bill Clinton on December 1, 1978.*

## A Young Man with Promise

Following high school graduation, Clinton studied international affairs at Georgetown University. In his senior year, he was awarded a Rhodes scholarship, which enabled him to study at Oxford University in England. Upon his return, he attended Yale University where he earned his law degree. It was there, at Yale University, where he met Hillary Rodham.

They married in 1975, and became parents when their daughter Chelsea was born on February 27, 1980.

After working on political campaigns for others, Clinton became attorney general of Arkansas in 1976. He won the election for governor of Arkansas two years later. At the age of 32, he was the youngest ever to hold that office. In 1980 he lost his reelection bid, but regained the governor's office in 1982 and served until he won the presidential election for the United States in 1992.

# William J. Clinton

## The 42nd President

Upon defeating Republican incumbent George H.W. Bush, Clinton became the 42nd president and the first president from the Democratic Party in 12 years. His first term of office was marked by great successes, disappointments, and the scandals that, in his second term, would lead to his impeachment by the House of Representatives and trial by the Senate.

Although there were more Democrats than Republicans in Congress during Clinton's first two years as president, he found it difficult to gain congressional approval for his plans. His biggest disappointment came with the defeat of his and First Lady Hillary Rodham Clinton's proposal to change the health care system by providing health care security for all.

The killing of 18 American soldiers on a peacekeeping mission to Somalia added to the nation's lack of confidence in Clinton's leadership. At the end of his first year in office a *Time/CNN* public opinion poll showed him to be the most unpopular first-year president in the history of polling.

Clinton pressed on, putting his energy into reducing the 254 billion dollar budget deficit that he had inherited with the presidency.

The House and the Senate approved his economic plan in 1993 by the margin of one vote in the House of Representatives and one vote in the Senate. By 1996 the deficit had been cut to 117 billion dollars and the economy was thriving.

## Common Ground

The congressional election of 1994 gave the Republican Party a majority of seats in both the House of Representatives and the Senate for the first time since the 1950s. After political standoffs, Clinton and Congress learned to work together. Clinton focused on "our relentless search for common ground," as he put it in his 1996 State of the Union Address.

*President Bill Clinton, Tipper Gore, Vice President Al Gore, and First Lady Hillary Rodham Clinton*

### Words to Know

**impeachment** (im-PEECH-muhnt): A legal statement of charges which is the first step in the possible removal of a president from office. If the House votes to impeach, the Senate then holds a trial; if found guilty, the president is removed from office.

**deficit** (DEF-uh-sit): When the government spends more money than it takes in.

While running for the presidency in 1996 against Republican presidential candidate Bob Dole and Reform Party candidate Ross Perot, Clinton signed four bills that addressed the common ground. These bills tightened immigration regulations, made health insurance more responsive to the needs of new mothers, imposed limits on welfare aid to the poor, and raised the minimum wage.

By championing causes that appealed to voters of both major parties, Clinton's presidency and his 1996 reelection campaign enjoyed great success. His moderate policies combined with the strong economy to make The Comeback Kid unbeatable.

## Investigations

Bill Clinton won the election to his second term of office in November 1996, winning 379 electoral votes to Dole's 159. Ross Perot earned zero electoral votes. Yet, doubts about his character that had emerged in his first term continued to impact his presidency. Suspect campaign contributions to the Democratic Party during the 1996 campaign led to a lengthy investigation. No charges were ever filed but the scandal hurt the president's reputation.

A civil suit filed by Paula Corbin Jones in 1994 accused Clinton of sexually harassing and assaulting her while he was governor of Arkansas and she was a state employee. A May 1998 trial date ensured that the investigation into Clinton's personal conduct would continue for many years. Ultimately, the courts dismissed the case in 1998 due to insufficient evidence and it never went to trial.

By the 1996 election, more than 25 million dollars had been spent researching the Clintons' involvement in Whitewater, a real estate deal gone sour. The scandal gained momentum in 1994 when Kenneth Starr, a political conservative, took charge of the investigation as special counsel.

*President Clinton signs the Health Insurance Portability and Accountability Act (HIPPA) in 1996.*

*President Clinton is sworn in for his second term of office with daughter Chelsea at his side and with his wife Hillary holding the family Bible during the proceedings.*

## Vice President Albert Gore, Jr.

Albert Gore, Jr., was born on March 31, 1948. He grew up in Carthage, Tennessee, and Washington, D.C. His father, Albert Sr., was a member of the United States Senate. His mother, Pauline LaFon Gore, was one of the first women to graduate from Vanderbilt Law School.

Gore graduated with honors from Harvard University in 1969. He then enlisted in the army and served in Vietnam. After his tour of duty, he became an investigative reporter for *The Tennessean* in Nashville. He also attended Vanderbilt University Divinity School and Vanderbilt Law School.

Elizabeth Aitcheson (nicknamed "Tipper") married Gore in 1970. The family grew to include four children: Karenna, Kristin, Sarah, and Albert III.

The people of Tennessee elected Gore to the House of Representatives, where he served from 1977 to 1985. He won election to the Tennessee Senate in 1984 and again in 1990, where he served until his vice-presidential term began in 1993.

In 2000, as his second vice-presidential term came to an end, Gore won the Democratic Party's nomination for president, but George W. Bush defeated him in a hard-fought election. After several weeks of challenges and debates regarding the counting of votes, Gore conceded the election to Bush. In his concession speech, the vice president said, "I know that many of my supporters are disappointed. I am, too, but our disappointment must be overcome by our love of country."

Following the loss in 2000, Gore went on to speak out for environmental protection and care for the Earth. He won the Nobel Peace Prize in 2007 along with an Emmy Award for his work on a program called *Current TV*. He starred in the documentary *An Inconvenient Truth* which won an Academy Award in 2007.

---

Kenneth Starr and Paula Corbin Jones would later play important roles in Clinton's impeachment during his second term. The presidency that was uplifted by prosperity and that improved America's leadership role in the world had also become a presidency marred by scandal.

# William J. Clinton

## Hard Work & Accomplishments

In February 1997, members of the House and Senate budget committees began work on the 1998 budget. Two of the president's most important budget proposals were a new program to provide health insurance for children and to increase educational funding by more than 50 billion dollars.

Both sides wanted to include a plan to reduce the deficit and set government spending on a course to achieve a balanced budget by 2002. Their goal was to work toward a point where the money taken in by the government equaled the money paid out.

The previous two years, Clinton and his staffers had been unable to agree on the budget. Their political showdowns had led to government shutdowns and hardships for the American people. Now the pressure was on for the two sides to finalize the 1998 budget.

On August 5, 1997, President Clinton signed the 1998 budget plan. They had finally come to an agreement; there would be no government shutdown. Both sides were pleased. The 1998 budget plan included the largest children's health care expansion in 30 years and the education increase the president had sought. It also contained the 500 dollar per-child tax break and other tax reductions that had been cornerstones of the Republican plan. In addition to that achievement, the success of the 1998 budget and the strong economy led a year later to the passage of the first balanced budget in 30 years, three years ahead of schedule.

*Clinton vetoed 17 bills during his first term of office and 20 in his second.*

*President Clinton signs a memorandum on outreach actions to increase employment of adults with disabilities.*

The summer of 1997 was a prosperous and hopeful time for the United States. Unemployment was down. Teen pregnancies were down and immunizations were up. In April, at Clinton's urging, Congress ratified the Chemical Weapons Convention, an international treaty that prohibits countries from manufacturing, using, or storing chemical weapons.

## America's Mission

It appeared that Clinton and Congress had learned to work together, fulfilling the promise described by the president in his second-term inaugural address the previous January. In that address, he stated that the American people returned to office a president of one party and a Congress of another. Clinton believed they did this as a call to work together and move on with America's mission.

However, this harmonious period soon gave way to one of the most divisive in American politics. Scandals arising from Clinton's personal behavior and his public denials led to investigations encouraged by many in Congress. Suspicion between the Democratic White House and Republican-led Congress politically split the nation and made it increasingly difficult to govern.

## Social Security

At the end of his second term, Clinton listed Social Security and Medicare reform as two of the most important issues overlooked by the distractions of scandal and impeachment. For a time however, it appeared that both parties were going to work together to change Social Security, a program that pays monthly checks to about 44 million Americans who are retired, disabled, or widowed. Due to the aging population, the government expected Social Security to go bankrupt in 2032.

On January 27, 1998, Clinton presented his goals for the future in a stirring State of the Union speech. Only six days had passed since the news media had reported suspicions of an extramarital affair between him and a young federal employee. In his speech, Clinton made no mention of the scandal. He focused instead on his ideas for the nation. Democrats applauded and Republicans sat silent as the president discussed the possibility of a budget surplus in coming years. Republicans had been talking about using the surplus for a tax cut, but Clinton urged Congress to save Social Security first.

Suddenly, Republican Newt Gingrich, the Speaker of the House and Clinton's major rival during much of his presidency, stood and applauded the idea of reserving money for Social Security. When they saw the most powerful Republican in Congress clapping, most Republicans followed his lead. Through paying attention to the country's problems rather than his own issues, Clinton had won the day.

Despite the promising start, talks over how to save Social Security soon stalled as government attention turned to the scandal and the impeachment process. By the time Clinton left office, the expectation was for Social Security to go bankrupt in 2037.

## Medicare

The president had hoped for a larger-scale overhaul of health insurance and Medicare than he was able to accomplish. A government health program, Medicare helps provide medical insurance for persons over 65 years of age and some disabled persons under 65.

Clinton bypassed Congress and achieved some success in 1998 with an expansion of patient protections covered by all federal health plans. These included the biggest changes in Medicare since it began. He made changes through an Executive Memorandum and by alterations in health care rules because neither memorandums nor rule changes needed the approval of Congress. Clinton was able to act as he thought best.

## Foreign Policy

Even Clinton's military decisions were overshadowed by accusations in the news that he was trying to deflect attention away from personal scandal. On August 20, 1998, Clinton ordered air strikes in retaliation against a terrorist organization that had bombed two U.S. embassies in Africa. The attack destroyed the terrorist base in Afghanistan and a reputed chemical weapons factory in Sudan. This occurred on the same day that testimony was being given in the investigation into allegations of a presidential extramarital affair.

In December 1998, the beginning of the debate in the House of Representatives to decide whether Clinton should be impeached was postponed by one day due to the U.S. bombing of Iraq. The president had ordered the air raids after Iraq refused to allow United Nations inspectors to search for weapons of mass destruction. "It is obvious that he is doing this for political reasons, and I and others are outraged," said Gerald Solomon, a Republican congressional leader.

General Henry Shelton, chairman of the Joint Chiefs of Staff, countered the accusation stating, "Militarily it was the right decision, the right date, and that decision was made back in November."

Clinton enjoyed acclaim for his success in brokering peace in Northern Ireland. He fostered talks between the various political and religious factions in Ireland and United Kingdom Prime Minister Tony Blair's government. These negotiations climaxed in the Good Friday Agreement that hammered out a power-sharing arrangement between the British-sponsored Irish government and rebels in Northern Ireland.

Voters across Ireland ratified the agreement in May 1998. The agreement was designed to end 30 years of conflict in which 3,400 people had died. Although Britain suspended the power-sharing institutions in February 2000 due to struggles over disarmament, the will to continue negotiations remains. "That agreement remains the very best hope we have ever had for making peace, and I still believe it will succeed," said the president.

# William J. Clinton

*President Clinton attends the Southern Regional Economics Conference.*

## Investigations & Impeachment

What makes a successful president? Is it the character of leadership that matters most or the decisions a leader makes on behalf of the country? The 1996 Republican platform, an expression of ideas most important to the Republican Party, urged the importance of moral clarity in our culture and ethical leadership in the White House. The 1996 Democratic platform stressed Bill Clinton's positive decisions during his first term and emphasized opportunity, responsibility, and community as the values that made America strong.

Investigations into the lives of the nation's leaders explored private behavior because all actions, both personal and public, were seen as important indicators of character. Public testimony about private matters filled the news. Democrats and Republicans accused each other of using scandal and investigations of government officials as a way of pushing them from power.

President Clinton was under constant investigation by an independent counsel from early 1994 to the end of his term in 2001. An independent counsel is a special prosecutor chosen to look into possible criminal conduct by high public officials. Independent counsel Kenneth Starr, prosecutor for most of the investigations, described his role in a 1999 *Newshour* interview. He said he had faithfully served the principles of our legal system, tried zealously to find out the relevant facts, assessed those facts in a very professional way, and then made sound judgments.

In a 1998 interview with the *Today* show, First Lady Hillary Rodham Clinton criticized Starr's investigations. She described Starr as a politically motivated prosecutor who was allied with the right-wing opponents of her husband. She stated that it was a very unfortunate turn of events that the criminal justice system was being used to try to achieve political ends.

*Floor proceedings of the U.S. Senate, in session during the impeachment trial of Bill Clinton.*

## Whitewater

The first investigation, called Whitewater, focused on an unprofitable Arkansas land deal the Clintons made in 1978 and their ties to a failed savings and loan. Under Starr's management, the scope of the independent counsel's investigation expanded far beyond Arkansas real estate. Starr accused the Clintons of hiding the truth by lying under oath, pressuring others to lie, and withholding the First Lady's billing records from work she performed for the savings and loan.

After spending more than 50 million dollars on many investigations, the independent counsel's office finally wrapped up the Whitewater inquiry in September 2000 without bringing charges against the Clintons. However, the courts convicted the Clintons' Whitewater business partners, James and Susan McDougal, of fraud in 1996.

The American people had never expressed much concern about Whitewater or other scandals. A *Washington Post-ABC News* poll showed that only slightly more than half of those questioned considered Whitewater to be an important issue. At the beginning of 1997, the president was more popular than at any time since his first inauguration.

*Linda Tripp is the Pentagon employee whose secret tape recordings of former White House intern Monica Lewinsky triggered a criminal investigation of President Clinton.*

## Consequences of Dishonesty

One year later the president's troubles were about to explode. Linda Tripp, a career government employee, had secretly taped personal conversations with a 24-year-old federal employee named Monica Lewinsky. She had recorded an unknowing Lewinsky talking about an alleged extramarital affair with the president.

In early January, Lewinsky had signed an affidavit, a legal written testimony, denying that she and the president had ever had sexual relations. This testimony was given in a civil case brought by Paula Jones against Clinton. Lawyers for the Jones case had been looking for a pattern of inappropriate behavior by the president to bolster charges of sexual harassment. Tripp believed she had proof that Lewinsky had lied and that the president was an adulterer. She phoned independent counsel Starr and told him about the tapes.

## William J. Clinton

On January 16, 1998, Starr received permission from a trio of federal judges to check whether Lewinsky had lied under oath, a crime called perjury. The judges also enabled him to question whether forces at the White House had encouraged Lewinsky to lie, a crime known as obstruction of justice.

That same day, agents from the Federal Bureau of Investigation (FBI) and U.S. attorneys questioned Lewinsky, pressuring her to testify against Clinton. Many months after the questioning, she accepted immunity and avoided prosecution by testifying against Clinton.

*President Clinton apologized to the country for his conduct in the Monica Lewinsky affair and said he would accept a congressional censure or rebuke.*

*Monica Lewinsky leaves Los Angeles with her lawyer, William Ginsburg.*

On January 17, 1998, Clinton testified that he had never had an affair with Monica Lewinsky.

The story of the president and the former White House intern dominated the press for more than a year.

After months of denying his affair with Lewinsky, on August 17, Clinton testified before a grand jury about their relationship. That night on national television, Clinton admitted to having an inappropriate relationship with Lewinsky. He further stated that he did not ask anyone to lie or break the law. He deeply regretted misleading the public and his family.

He labeled the Jones lawsuit as politically inspired, and criticized Starr's independent counsel investigation. He said even presidents have private lives and it was time to get on with our national life.

Less than a month later, Starr submitted his referral on the scandal to Congress. The House of Representatives began their impeachment inquiry.

Starr disagreed with the president's assertion that the investigation was about prying into private lives. In an appearance before the House Judiciary Committee, Starr explained his accusation. "The evidence suggests that the president chose to engage in a criminal act, to reach an understanding with Ms. Lewinsky that they would both make false statements under oath… This was no longer an issue of private conduct."

## Impeachment

After months of testimony, the House Judiciary Committee approved four articles of impeachment in a vote that pitted Republicans against Democrats. Two of the articles accused Clinton of perjury. Article One alleged that the president lied to the grand jury in August. Article Two asserted that he lied during his testimony in the Jones case. Article Three charged Clinton with obstruction of justice. It claimed he encouraged Lewinsky and others to lie and hide evidence. Article Four asserted that the president abused his power by deceiving the people of the United States, members of Congress, and other governmental employees.

Each article of impeachment ended with the statement, "William Jefferson Clinton, by such conduct, warrants impeachment and trial and removal from office and disqualification to hold and enjoy any office of honor, trust, or profit under the United States."

The American public had another opinion. In a *CNN/USA Today/Gallup* poll taken on the day of the committee vote, only a little more than a third of the people polled thought that the committee should vote to impeach. More than half of the people polled (58%) believed the president should receive censure, an official expression of disapproval.

On December 19, 1998, the House of Representatives approved impeachment on two of the four articles. Article One, the perjury charge that addressed

*Independent Counsel Kenneth Starr is sworn in before the House Judiciary Committee Thursday, November 19, 1998, at the start of the impeachment inquiry against President Clinton. Starr's testimony marks the first time that the independent counsel has been available for questioning for his investigation against Clinton.*

Clinton's testimony before the grand jury, passed with a vote of 228 to 206. Article Three, which accused the president of obstruction of justice, passed with a vote of 221 to 212. Most Republicans voted for impeachment and most Democrats voted against it. Clinton became the first president since Andrew Johnson to be impeached.

## Kenneth Starr

Attorney Kenneth Starr was selected to serve as independent counsel, a job in which he would investigate several issues that involved President Bill Clinton and others.

Kenneth Starr was born on July 21, 1946, in Vernon, Texas. He earned degrees from three different universities, finally receiving his law degree from Duke University. Starr married Alice Jean Mendell in 1970 and they later had three children together.

A former judge who served in both the Ronald Reagan and George H.W. Bush administrations, Starr originally was hired to lead an investigation called Whitewater, which involved real estate deals that Bill and Hillary Clinton and others had made. Based on evidence that Starr uncovered, three people, former Arkansas Governor Jim Guy Tucker, and Jim and Susan McDougal, were convicted of crimes in May of 1996.

Starr also investigated Travelgate, which was based on claims that Hillary Clinton had improperly fired the staff that ran the White House travel office. He also looked into Filegate, which accused the Clintons of acquiring hundreds of FBI files. The Clintons were not charged with crimes in either case.

In addition, Starr investigated the death of Deputy White House Counsel Vince Foster, Jr., who died in July of 1993. Foster's death had been ruled a suicide by Starr's predecessor. But because enough people believed the death was a murder, Starr reopened the investigation. In 1997, Starr closed the case, finding that Foster had indeed killed himself.

Finally, Starr investigated whether President Clinton had an improper relationship with White House intern Monica Lewinsky. This relationship led to numerous other charges against the president, including lying under oath, obstruction of justice, and abuse of power.

In September 1998, Starr made a report to Congress detailing the reasons why the president should be impeached. Based on Starr's report, the House of Representatives voted to impeach Clinton. The Senate ultimately found him not guilty.

On Oct. 18, 1999, Starr left his job as independent counsel, saying he wished to return to his law practice, continue teaching at New York University, and finish a book on the Supreme Court that he had started before accepting the position of independent counsel.

His book, *First Among Equals: The Supreme Court in American Life*, was written to help Americans better understand the Supreme Court. He published it in 2003.

# William J. Clinton

*House Democrats leave the House Chambers on Capitol Hill, as voting on the first article of impeachment against President Clinton began. The Democrats briefly walked out of the chamber in protest when Republicans blocked their effort to force a vote on the lesser penalty of censure as an alternative to impeachment.*

Thirteen Republicans were chosen as House managers. They would act as prosecutors against Clinton in his Senate impeachment trial on the two charges. Democrats, who had largely favored censure over impeachment, refused to join the team of managers.

The president was as popular as he had ever been. In a *CBS News/New York Times* poll concluded the day after the impeachment, 72% of the people who responded said they approved of the way Clinton was handling his job as president. In contrast, 58% said they looked unfavorably upon the Republican Party. It was the highest disapproval rating ever recorded in the 14 years the question had been asked.

## Trial in the Senate

The impeachment trial began January 7, 1999. It was presided over by the Supreme Court Chief Justice William Rehnquist. The senators were the jurors. In order to convict Clinton and remove him from office, two thirds of the Senate, 67 out of 100 senators, would need to vote guilty on at least one of the two articles of impeachment.

The House managers argued that the president had broken the law by committing perjury and obstruction of justice.

They tried to convince the Senate that his actions were high crimes and misdemeanors, the criteria for impeachment laid out by the founding fathers of the United States. The president's lawyers argued that the president did not commit perjury in his grand jury testimony, did not obstruct justice, and did not deserve to be removed from office.

Following weeks of arguments and three days of secret discussion, the Senate was ready to vote on the two articles of impeachment that had been approved by the House of Representatives. On February 12, 1999, the senators were asked to render their verdicts. In both cases, the senators did not cast enough guilty votes. The president was acquitted of all charges and would not be removed from office.

# William J. Clinton

In a speech after the Senate's verdict, Clinton said, "I want to say again to the American people how profoundly sorry I am for what I said and did to trigger these events and the great burden they have imposed on the Congress and the American people."

In 2001, Clinton admitted he had given false testimony when questioned in the Jones case about the Lewinsky affair. He paid a $25,000 fine and gave up his law license for five years in order to avoid prosecution for perjury and obstruction of justice.

Clinton talked about what his ordeal had taught him in an interview before the Ministers' Leadership Conference. "I had to come to terms with a lot of things about the fundamental importance of character and integrity," he said. "It's been an amazing encounter, you know, trying to rebuild my family life, which is the most important thing of all."

*First Lady Hillary Rodham Clinton watches President Clinton pause as he thanks those Democratic members of the House of Representatives who voted against impeachment in this December 19, 1998 photo.*

## Bill Clinton's Legacy

On March 24, 1999, the United States and other members of the North Atlantic Treaty Organization (NATO) launched an air war in Yugoslavia. For 78 days, NATO forces bombed the army of Yugoslavian President Slobodan Milosevic. NATO's objectives were to end the violence against ethnic Albanians in Kosovo and to provide for the safe return of all refugees and other displaced people. Ethnic hatred had led to the war, and multinational cooperation led by Clinton had stopped it.

*President Clinton maintained communication with the leaders of the North Atlantic Treaty Organization (NATO) to resolve issues in Kosovo.*

Following a November 1999 trip to the war-torn region of Kosovo in Yugoslavia with his daughter Chelsea, President Clinton spoke of racial diversity in the American military as a model of a genuine community, where everyone receives equal treatment. "The power of their example could have as big an impact on the people of Kosovo as the force of their arms," he said in an interview with the *Christian Science Monitor*.

Clinton's policy earned vindication by democratic elections held in Yugoslavia on September 24, 2000. Milosevic was defeated by Vojislav Kostunica. When Milosevic tried to invalidate the election, the Yugoslav people demonstrated against him, ending his 13-year dictatorship. "Democracy has reclaimed every piece of ground he took," said a celebratory Clinton in the White House Rose Garden.

## Globalization

The same week that democracy triumphed in Yugoslavia, Clinton signed an agreement allowing China to join the World Trade Organization. The president had pushed for China's inclusion because he recognized its importance as a trading partner and growing world power. He also hoped for improvements in China's record on human rights, a hope that still has not been realized.

Clinton's push for world trade and globalization backfired on him at the World Trade Organization meeting in Seattle, Washington, in November 1999. Thousands of protestors disrupted the meeting, expressing their concern over such issues as workers' rights and protection of the environment. Clinton assured them that labor standards and the environment would be protected.

# William J. Clinton

However, while his assurances did not carry much weight with the demonstrators, the leaders of developing countries took his comments as a sign that he would try to keep them from selling their goods in the United States unless they met certain criteria. The meeting ended in failure.

Another area of mixed success in foreign policy was Clinton's involvement in the peace process between Israel and Palestine. In 1993, 1997, and 1998 he succeeded in negotiating agreements between the two countries. However, talks stalled at the U.S. historic site of Camp David during the summer of 2000. That fall, hostilities broke out between the two enemies, leaving more than 350 dead.

Days before the end of his presidency, Clinton pressured Israeli Prime Minister Ehud Barak and Palestinian leader Yasser Arafat to discuss a Clinton-proposed peace deal that would parcel out control over disputed land. *Time Magazine* reported that Clinton told Arafat, "If you don't take this golden opportunity, you will have no mention in history and coming generations of Palestinians will curse you." Arafat and Barak agreed to negotiate.

*Israeli Prime Minister Yitzhak Rabin (at left) and Palestine Liberation Organization chairman Yasir Arafat (at right) shook hands at the historic 1993 signing of the Middle East Peace Agreement.*

# William J. Clinton

## Never Give Up

"One of the things that I greatly admire about him is the guy never gives up," said John Podesta, the president's chief of staff for the last two years of his term, in an interview with Chris Bury. In the waning days of his presidency Clinton set aside lands as national monuments to protect them from development, changed Forest Service rules to place a ban on new roads in certain wilderness areas such as old-growth forests, and expanded protected areas by invoking his executive privilege under the Antiquities Act. None of his last-minute environmental protections required congressional approval.

By the end of his term, he had protected more wild lands than any president since Theodore Roosevelt. "We have saved and restored some of our most glorious natural wonders, from Florida's Everglades to Hawaii's coral reefs, from the redwoods of California to the red rock canyons of Utah," he said.

Clinton's dedication has helped society make the transition from an industrial era into the information age. His administration supported the computer revolution with tax breaks, computers for schools, privacy regulations, and an anti-trust lawsuit against industry giant Microsoft that alleged the company used its strength to suppress competition. More than 30% of the economic growth of the country during Clinton's presidency has been attributed to advances in high technology.

Clinton and Federal Reserve chairman Alan Greenspan receive credit for ushering

*President Clinton*

in a tremendous period of prosperity. Conversations with Greenspan early on led Clinton to successfully focus on reduction of the national debt. In his 2000 State of the Union speech, the president noted that America had achieved the longest period of economic growth in our entire history.

In an interview at the Ministers' Leadership Conference at the end of his presidency, Clinton joked that what he would miss most about not being president is "having the Marine Band play 'Hail to the Chief' every time you walk in a room." Then he said, "But what I will miss more than anything else is the job. You know, I loved the job. I love it every day. My biggest problem now is I hate to go to sleep at night. ...I'm trying to get everything done I can do before I leave. I have loved the work."

# William J. Clinton

## First Lady Hillary Rodham Clinton

Hillary Rodham Clinton was one of the most active and divisive First Ladies in history. She worked tirelessly on behalf of children, fulfilling her belief that "we all have an obligation to give something of ourselves to our community."

Born on October 26, 1947, Hillary Diane Rodham grew up in Park Ridge, Illinois, with her parents, Hugh and Dorothy, and two younger brothers, Hugh Jr., and Tony. As a child, she was a Girl Scout. While First Lady, she served as honorary president of the Girl Scouts of America.

After graduation from Wellesley College in 1969, she enrolled in Yale Law School, where she met fellow student Bill Clinton. The two were married in 1975. They have one daughter, Chelsea.

At Yale, she met Marian Wright Edelman, founder of the Children's Defense Fund. After graduation, Rodham worked for the organization and later served as its chairperson.

A controversial first for a First Lady was Hillary's appointment as chair of President Clinton's 1993 health care plan. No other First Lady had been given this type of governmental position. In the end, the health care plan failed to pass and caused litigation against the Clinton White House regarding closed door sessions that Rodham Clinton was involved in.

The First Lady did have a positive impact on some health care issues, such as increasing the number of children vaccinated and increasing health insurance coverage for children whose parents could not otherwise afford it.

Another First Lady first came when Hillary announced that she would run for Senator of New York. On November 7, 2000, Hillary Rodham Clinton was elected to the United States Senate.

Then on January 20, 2007, Senator Clinton announced she would be seeking the democratic nomination for the 2008 presidential election, yet another First Lady first. She began campaigning and in the fall of 2007, national polls showed Clinton leading by wide margins. By Super Tuesday, February 5, 2008, the battle for the Democratic nomination was between Clinton and Barack Obama. On the final day of primaries, June 3, 2008, Obama had earned enough votes to become the presumptive nominee for the Democratic Party. Four days later, on June 7, Clinton suspended her campaign.

As Senator Obama continued his campaign to win the presidency through the summer and fall of 2008, Hillary and Bill Clinton gave the Obama-Biden ticket their endorsement and joined them on the campaign trail. Many feel their support was key to Obama's victory in the 2008 election.

# Looking Back, and Forward

Ronald Reagan was the first president to complete two full terms of office after Dwight Eisenhower. An extremely popular man, Reagan had an approval rating of 68 percent when he left office, almost the same as when he had first taken office eight years before.

Many Americans thought that Reagan helped the country recapture the strength and optimism that it had lost. But the huge increase in the deficit severely weakened the United States and gave its citizens reason to believe that their optimism had been misguided. People were also concerned about the ethics of the Reagan administration. It was one of the most highly examined administrations in modern times. More than 100 officials were investigated for official misconduct or criminal violations. Reagan was so good at keeping any bad news about the people around him from sticking to him that he was called the Teflon President.

President Bush's finest hour came with the defeat of the Iraqi army in the spring of 1991. U.S. troops had performed well and, by leading a coalition of forces from other nations, they supported Bush's declaration of a New World Order. Bush appeared confident and capable of handling this international crisis. It was his handling of domestic affairs that was his downfall. He was perceived as being out of touch with Middle America, the people Bill Clinton appealed to in 1992.

Clinton's election was seen as an opportunity to get beyond gridlock, the situation in which Reagan and Bush had found themselves during their presidencies. Gridlock occurred for them because they were Republican presidents who had Democratic majorities controlling Congress. Clinton had a Democratic majority in both houses to work with during his first two years, but divisions within the party made it difficult for him to appear in control. After the dramatic Republican victories in both the House and the Senate in 1994, he had an even harder time.

Some people have suggested that Clinton had the added disadvantage of being in office at a time when the public had grown negative about the political process and its participants. People seemed to be just waiting for him to make a mistake.

Clinton was able to battle back from extremely low approval ratings in the polls after his first year in office to defeat Republican candidate Bob Dole in 1996. In his second term, for the first time in his political career, Clinton would be freed from the need to worry about being re-elected. Americans could now only hope that he would use this opportunity to tackle some of the most difficult problems the nation faced.

For over two hundred years, America has been led by many different individuals with many different styles. Some have had to fight enemies on foreign soil while others have had to deal with difficulties inside our own boundaries.

## Words to Know

**gridlock** (GRID-lok): A term for the stalemate that takes place when the executive branch of government is controlled by one party and the legislative branch is controlled by another, and neither is very successful in promoting its programs.

# Cabinet Members

## Reagan

**VICE PRESIDENT**
George H. W. Bush

**SECRETARY OF STATE**
Alexander M. Haig, Jr.
George P. Shultz

**SECRETARY OF THE TREASURY**
Donald T. Regan
James A. Baker, III
Nicholas F. Brady

**SECRETARY OF DEFENSE**
Caspar W. Weinberger
Frank C. Carlucci

**SECRETARY OF THE INTERIOR**
James G. Watt
William P. Clark
Donald P. Hodel

**SECRETARY OF AGRICULTURE**
John R. Block
Richard E. Lyng

**SECRETARY OF COMMERCE**
Malcolm Baldrige
C. William Verity, Jr.

**SECRETARY OF LABOR**
Raymond J. Donovan
William E. Brock
Ann Dore McLaughlin

**SECRETARY OF HEALTH
AND HUMAN SERVICES**
Richard S. Schweiker
Margaret M. Heckler
Otis R. Bowen

**SECRETARY OF HOUSING
AND URBAN DEVELOPMENT**
Samuel R. Pierce, Jr.

**SECRETARY OF TRANSPORTATION**
Andrew L. Lewis, Jr.
Elizabeth H. Dole
James H. Burnley 4th

**SECRETARY OF ENERGY**
James B. Edwards
Donald P. Hodel
John S. Herrington

**SECRETARY OF EDUCATION**
T. H. Bell
William J. Bennett
Lauro F. Cavazos

## Bush

**VICE PRESIDENT**
Dan Quayle

**SECRETARY OF STATE**
James A. Baker, III
Lawrence S. Eagleburger

**SECRETARY OF THE TREASURY**
Nicholas F. Brady

**SECRETARY OF DEFENSE**
Richard Cheney

**ATTORNEY GENERAL**
Richard L. Thornburgh
William P. Barr

**SECRETARY OF THE INTERIOR**
Manuel Lujan Jr.

**SECRETARY OF AGRICULTURE**
Clayton K. Yeutter
Edward Madigan

**SECRETARY OF COMMERCE**
Robert A. Mosbacher Sr..
Barbara H. Franklin

**SECRETARY OF LABOR**
Elizabeth H. Dole
Lynn Martin

**SECRETARY OF HEALTH
AND HUMAN SERVICES**
Louis W. Sullivan

**SECRETARY OF HOUSING
AND URBAN DEVELOPMENT**
Jack F. Kemp

**SECRETARY OF TRANSPORTATION**
Samuel K. Skinner
Andrew Card

**SECRETARY OF ENERGY**
James D. Watkins

**SECRETARY OF EDUCATION**
Lauro F. Cavazos
Lamar Alexander

**SECRETARY OF VETERANS AFFAIRS**
Edward J. Derwinski

★ ★ ★

## Clinton

**VICE PRESIDENT**
Albert A. Gore Jr.

**SECRETARY OF STATE**
Warren M. Christopher
Madeleine Albright

**SECRETARY OF THE TREASURY**
Lloyd Bentsen
Robert E. Rubin
Lawrence H. Summers

**SECRETARY OF DEFENSE**
Les Aspin
William J. Perry
William S. Cohen

**ATTORNEY GENERAL**
Janet Reno

**SECRETARY OF THE INTERIOR**
Bruce Babbitt

**SECRETARY OF AGRICULTURE**
Mike Espy
Dan Glickman

**SECRETARY OF COMMERCE**
Ronald H. Brown
Mickey Kantor
William M. Daley
Norman Y. Mineta

**SECRETARY OF LABOR**
Robert B. Reich
Alexis Herman

**SECRETARY OF HEALTH
AND HUMAN SERVICES**
Donna E. Shalala

**SECRETARY OF HOUSING
AND URBAN DEVELOPMENT**
Henry G. Cisneros
Andrew M. Cuomo

**SECRETARY OF TRANSPORTATION**
Federico F. Pena
Rodney Slater

**SECRETARY OF ENERGY**
Hazel R. O'Leary
Frederico F. Pena
Bill Richardson

**SECRETARY OF EDUCATION**
Richard W. Riley

**SECRETARY OF VETERANS AFFAIRS**
Jesse Brown
Togo D. West, Jr.

# Timeline

**1770**

1774 — First Continental Congress

1775 — American Revolution begins

1776 — America declares independence from Great Britain

**1780**

1783 — Treaty of Paris formally ends American Revolution

1787 — U.S. Constitution is written

**1789 — George Washington becomes president**

**1790**

1791 — Bill of Rights becomes part of Constitution

1793 — Eli Whitney invents cotton gin

**1797 — John Adams becomes president**

**1800**

1800 — Washington, D.C., becomes permanent U.S. capital

**1801 — Thomas Jefferson becomes president**

1803 — Louisiana Purchase almost doubles size of the United States

1808 — Slave trade ends

**1809 — James Madison becomes president**

**1810**

1812 — War of 1812 begins

1814 — British burn Washington, D.C. War of 1812 fighting ends

1815 — Treaty of Ghent officially ends War of 1812

**1817 — James Monroe becomes president**

**1820**

1820 — Missouri Compromise is passed

1823 — Monroe Doctrine is issued

**1825 — John Quincy Adams becomes president**

1828 — Popular votes used for first time to help elect a president

**1829 — Andrew Jackson becomes president**

# Timeline

**1830**

- **1830** Congress passes Indian Removal Act
- **1832** Samuel Morse has idea for telegraph
- **1835** Samuel Colt patents revolver
- **1837** Martin Van Buren becomes president
- **1838** Native Americans are forced to move to Oklahoma traveling Trail of Tears

**1840**

- **1841** William Harrison becomes president
  John Tyler becomes president
- **1845** James Polk becomes president
- **1845** Texas is annexed to United States
- **1846** Mexican War begins
  Boundary between Canada and United States is decided
- **1848** Gold is discovered in California
  First women's rights convention is held
- **1849** Zachary Taylor becomes president

**1850**

- **1850** Millard Fillmore becomes president
- **1850** Compromise of 1850 is passed
- **1853** Franklin Pierce becomes president
- **1857** James Buchanan becomes president

**1860**

- **1860** Southern states begin to secede from Union
- **1861** Abraham Lincoln becomes president
- **1863** Abraham Lincoln gives Gettysburg Address
- **1865** Andrew Johnson becomes president
- **1865** Civil War ends
  Freedman's Bureau is created
  13th Amendment abolishes slavery
- **1868** Impeachment charges are brought against President Johnson
- **1869** Ulysses S. Grant becomes president

**1870**

- **1873** U.S. economy collapses; depression begins
- **1876** Alexander Graham Bell invents telephone
- **1877** Rutherford Hayes becomes president
- **1879** Thomas Edison invents light bulb

**1880**

- **1881** James Garfield becomes president
  Chester Arthur becomes president
- **1882** Chinese Exclusion Act restricts number of Chinese immigrants allowed into United States
- **1885** Grover Cleveland becomes president
- **1889** Benjamin Harrison becomes president

# Timeline

## 1890

**1890** — U.S. troops kill more than 200 Sioux and Cheyenne at Wounded Knee

**1893** — Grover Cleveland becomes president again

**1893** — Charles and J. Frank Duryea construct first car in the United States

**1897** — William McKinley becomes president

**1898** — Spanish-American War occurs

## 1900

**1901** — Theodore Roosevelt becomes president

**1903** — Orville and Wilbur Wright fly their plane at Kitty Hawk, North Carolina

**1908** — Henry Ford produces Model T

**1909** — William H. Taft becomes president

## 1910

**1913** — Woodrow Wilson becomes president

**1914** — Panama Canal opens

**1917** — America enters World War I

**1919** — World War I ends

## 1920

**1920** — 19th Amendment gives women right to vote

**1921** — Warren Harding becomes president

**1923** — Calvin Coolidge becomes president

**1927** — Charles Lindbergh makes first nonstop flight across Atlantic

**1929** — Herbert Hoover becomes president

**1929** — Stock market crashes; America enters economic depression

## 1930

**1933** — Franklin D. Roosevelt becomes president

**1939** — World War II begins

## 1940

**1941** — Pearl Harbor is bombed; America enters World War II

**1945** — Harry S. Truman becomes president

**1945** — United States drops atomic bombs on Hiroshima and Nagasaki; World War II ends; United Nations is formed

# Timeline

**1950**

- **1950** Korean War begins
- **1953** Dwight Eisenhower becomes president
- **1953** Korean War ends
- **1954** Supreme Court orders desegregation of schools
- **1957** Soviet Union launches *Sputnik I*
- **1958** United States launches *Explorer I*; NASA is created

**1960**

- **1961** John F. Kennedy becomes president
- **1962** Cuban Missile Crisis
- **1963** Lyndon Johnson becomes president
- **1964** Civil Rights Act of 1964 is passed
- **1965** First U.S. troops sent to Vietnam War
- **1968** Martin Luther King, Jr. is assassinated
- **1969** Richard Nixon becomes president
- **1969** Neil Armstrong is first person to walk on moon

**1970**

- **1970** First Earth Day is celebrated
- **1973** OPEC places oil embargo resulting in fuel shortages
- **1974** Nixon is first president to resign
- **1974** Gerald Ford becomes president
- **1975** War in Vietnam ends
- **1976** America celebrates its bicentennial
- **1977** Jimmy Carter becomes president
- **1978** Leaders of Israel and Egypt sign the Camp David Accords
- **1979** U.S. embassy in Iran is attacked and hostages are taken

**1980**

- **1981** Ronald Reagan becomes president
- **1981** American hostages are released; Reagan appoints first woman to Supreme Court, Sandra Day O'Connor
- **1986** U.S. space shuttle *Challenger* explodes after lift-off
- **1989** George H. W. Bush becomes president

**1990**

- **1991** Persian Gulf War occurs
- **1992** U.S. troops are sent to Somalia to lead multinational relief force; Riots explode in Los Angeles
- **1993** William J. Clinton becomes president
- **1993** World Trade Center is bombed by terrorists
- **1995** Bomb destroys federal building in Oklahoma City
- **1998** U.S. bombs Iraq; Impeachment charges are brought against President Clinton
- **1999** First balanced budget in 30 years is passed; Impeachment trial ends

**2000**

- **2000** Clinton sets aside land for national parks and monuments; Outcome of the presidential race is clouded due to voting miscounts
- **2001** George W. Bush becomes president
- **2001** Terrorist Attack on the World Trade Center; President Bush announces War on Terrorism
- **2002** No Child Left Behind Act is signed into law
- **2003** U.S. troops are sent to Iraq
- **2009** Barack Obama becomes president

# Presidents of the United States

| President | Birth | Party | Term | Death |
|---|---|---|---|---|
| George Washington | February 22, 1732; Westmoreland Cty., VA | None | April 30, 1789 - March 4, 1797 | December 14, 1799; Mt. Vernon, VA |
| John Adams | October 30, 1735; Braintree (Quincy), MA | Federalist | March 4, 1797 - March 4, 1801 | July 4, 1826; Quincy, MA |
| Thomas Jefferson | April 13, 1743; Abermarle Cty., VA | Democratic-Republican | March 4, 1801 - March 4, 1809 | July 4, 1826; Charlottesville, VA |
| James Madison | March 16, 1751; Port Conway, VA | Democratic-Republican | March 4, 1809 - March 4, 1817 | June 28, 1836; Orange County, VA |
| James Monroe | April 28, 1758; Westmoreland Cty., VA | Democratic-Republican | March 4, 1817 - March 4, 1825 | July 4, 1831; New York, NY |
| John Quincy Adams | July 11, 1767; Braintree (Quincy), MA | Democratic-Republican | March 4, 1825 - March 4, 1829 | February 23, 1848; Washington, D.C |
| Andrew Jackson | March 15, 1767; Waxhaw, SC | Democratic | March 4, 1829 - March 4, 1837 | June 8, 1845; Nashville, TN |
| Martin Van Buren | December 5, 1782; Kinderhook, NY | Democratic | March 4, 1837 - March 4, 1841 | July 24, 1862; Kinderhook, NY |
| William Henry Harrison | February 9, 1773; Berkeley, VA | Whig | March 4, 1841 - April 4, 1841 | April 4, 1841; Washington, D.C. |
| John Tyler | March 29, 1790; Charles City Cty., VA | Whig | April 4, 1841 - March 4, 1845 | January 18, 1862; Richmond, VA |
| James Polk | November 2, 1795; Mecklenburg Cty., NC | Democratic | March 4, 1845 - March 4, 1849 | June 15, 1849; Nashville, TN |
| Zachary Taylor | November 24, 1784; Orange Cty., VA | Whig | March 4, 1849 - July 9, 1850 | July 9, 1850; Washington, D.C. |
| Millard Fillmore | January 7, 1800; Locke Township, NY | Whig | July 9, 1850 - March 4, 1853 | March 8, 1874; Buffalo, NY |
| Franklin Pierce | November 23, 1804; Hillsborough, NH | Democratic | March 4, 1853 - March 4, 1857 | October 8, 1869; Concord, NH |
| James Buchanan | April 23, 1791; Cove Gap, PA | Democratic | March 4, 1857 - March 4, 1861 | June 1, 1868; Lancaster, PA |
| Abraham Lincoln | February 12, 1809; Hardin Cty., KY | Republican | March 4, 1861 - April 15, 1865 | April 15, 1865; Washington, D.C. |
| Andrew Johnson | December 29, 1808; Raleigh, NC | Republican | April 15, 1865 - March 4, 1869 | July 31, 1875; Carter County, TN |
| Ulysses S. Grant | April 27, 1822; Point Pleasant, OH | Republican | March 4, 1869 - March 4, 1877 | July 23, 1885; Mount McGregor, NY |
| Rutherford B. Hayes | October 4, 1822; Delaware, OH | Republican | March 4, 1877 - March 4, 1881 | January 17, 1893; Fremont, OH |
| James Garfield | November 18, 1831; Orange, OH | Republican | March 4, 1881 - September 19, 1881 | September 19, 1881; Elberon, NJ |
| Chester Arthur | October 5, 1830; North Fairfield, VT | Republican | September 20, 1881 - March 4, 1885 | November 18, 1886; New York, NY |
| Grover Cleveland | March 18, 1837; Caldwell, NJ | Democratic | March 4, 1885 - March 4, 1889; March 4, 1893 - March 4, 1897 | June 24, 1908; Princeton, NJ |

# Presidents of the United States

| President | Birth | Party | Term | Death |
|---|---|---|---|---|
| Benjamin Harrison | August 20, 1833; North Bend, OH | Republican | March 4, 1889 - March 4, 1893 | March 13, 1901; Indianapolis, IN |
| William McKinley | January 29, 1843; Niles OH | Republican | March 4, 1897 - September 14, 1901 | September 14, 1901; Buffalo, NY |
| Theodore Roosevelt | October 27, 1858; New York, NY | Republican | September 14, 1901 - March 4, 1909 | January 6, 1919; Oyster Bay, NY |
| William H. Taft | September 15, 1857; Cincinnati, OH | Republican | March 4, 1909 - March 4, 1913 | March 8, 1930; Washington, D.C. |
| Woodrow Wilson | December 28, 1856; Staunton, VA | Democratic | March 4, 1913 - March 4, 1921 | February 3, 1924; Washington, D.C. |
| Warren Harding | November 2, 1865; Corsica, OH | Republican | March 4, 1921 - August 2, 1923 | August 2, 1923; San Francisco, CA |
| Calvin Coolidge | July 4, 1872; Plymouth, VT | Republican | August 3, 1923 - March 4, 1929 | January 5, 1933; Northampton, MA |
| Herbert Hoover | August 10, 1874; West Branch, IA | Republican | March 4, 1929 - March 4, 1933 | October 20, 1964; New York, NY |
| Franklin D. Roosevelt | January 30, 1882; Hyde Park, NY | Democratic | March 4, 1933 - April 12, 1945 | April 12, 1945; Warm Springs, GA |
| Harry S. Truman | May 8, 1884; Lamar, MO | Democratic | April 12, 1945 - January 20, 1953 | December 26, 1972; Kansas City, MO |
| Dwight Eisenhower | October 14, 1890; Denison, TX | Republican | January 20, 1953 - January 20, 1961 | March 28, 1969; Washington, D.C. |
| John F. Kennedy | May 29, 1917; Brookline, MA | Democratic | January 20, 1961 - November 22, 1963 | November 22, 1963; Dallas, TX |
| Lyndon Johnson | August 27, 1908; Stonewall, TX | Democratic | November 22, 1963 - January 20, 1969 | January 22, 1973; San Antonio, TX |
| Richard Nixon | January 9, 1913; Yorba Linda, CA | Republican | January 20, 1969 - August 9, 1974 | April 22, 1994; New York, NY |
| Gerald Ford | July 14, 1913; Omaha, NE | Republican | August 9, 1974 - January 20, 1977 | December 26, 2006; Rancho Mirage, CA |
| Jimmy Carter | October 1, 1924; Plains, GA | Democratic | January 20, 1977 - January 20, 1981 | |
| Ronald Reagan | February 6, 1911; Tampico, IL | Republican | January 20, 1981 - January 20, 1989 | June 5, 2004; Bel Air, CA |
| George H. W. Bush | June 12, 1924; Milton, MA | Republican | January 20, 1989 - January 20, 1993 | |
| William J. Clinton | August 19, 1946; Hope, AR | Democratic | January 20, 1993 - January 20, 2001 | |
| George W. Bush | July 6, 1946; New Haven, CT | Republican | January 20, 2001 - January 20, 2009 | |
| Barack Obama | August 4, 1961 Honolulu, Hawaii | Democratic | January 20, 2009 - | |

# Index

## A
acquired immune deficiency symdrome, 8
acquitted, 48
Afghanistan, 42
Africa, 42
Albanians, 50
Alfred P. Murrah Federal Building, 9
Alzheimer's disease, 21
An Inconvenient Truth, 39
Antiquities Act, 52
approval rating, 31, 32, 48, 54
Arafat, Yasser, 51

## B
bankruptcy, 28
Barak, Ehud, 51
Berlin Wall, 30
Blair, Tony, 42
Bowland Amendment, 20
Boys Nation, 36
budget deficit, 17, 28, 37
Bush, Barbara, 22, 29
Bush, George H. W., 3, 7, 21, 22-33, 37, 39, 47, 54, 55, 59, 61
    born, 22, 61
    First Lady, 22, 29
    term, 22, 61
    vice president, 22, 27, 32, 55

## C
cabinet, 55
Camp David, 51, 59
Carter, Jimmy, 4, 14, 15, 18, 26, 33, 36, 59, 61
censure, 45, 46, 48
Central Intelligence Agency, 25
Chemical Weapons Convention, 40
China, 25, 33, 50
Clinton, Hillary Rodham, 34, 37, 38, 43, 47, 49, 53
Clinton, William J., 3, 8, 9, 33, 34-52, 53, 54, 59, 61
    born, 34, 61
    First Lady, 34, 53
    term, 34, 61
    vice president, 34, 39, 55
Cold War, 30
Comeback Kid, 38
common ground, 37-38
concession, 39
conservative, 25, 32, 33, 38
Contras, 19-20

## D
deficit, 17, 28, 29, 37, 40, 54
deregulation, 17
drug trafficking, 30

## E
Eisenhower, Dwight D., 14, 54, 59, 61
environmental protection, 39, 52
Executive Memorandum, 42

## F
Federal Bureau of Investigation, 45
Ferraro, Geraldine, 18
feul shortages, 14, 59
Filegate, 47
Ford, Gerald, 14, 25, 33, 59, 61

## G
Gingrich, Newt, 41
Girls Nation, 36
Good Friday Agreement, 42
Gorbachev, Mikhail, 20, 30
Gore, Al, 34, 37, 39
Great Communicator, 15
Greenspan, Alan, 52
Grenada, 17
gridlock, 54

## H
health insurance, 38, 40, 42, 53
Hinkley, John Jr., 15
homelessness, 8
House Judiciary Committee, 45, 46
Hussein, Saddam, 30

## I
immigration, 38
immunity, 45
impeachment, 37, 39, 41, 43, 45, 46, 48, 49, 57, 59
inauguration, 4, 9, 44
independent counsel, 43, 44, 45, 46, 47
inflation, 13, 14
information age, 52
Intermediate-Range Nuclear Forces Treaty, 20
investigation, 20, 25, 38, 41, 42, 43, 44, 45, 46, 47
Iran, 14, 19, 20, 59
Iran-Contra scandal, 20
Iraq, 30, 31, 42, 54, 59
Isreal, 51, 59

## J
Johnson, Andrew, 46, 57, 60
Jones, Paula, 44
Just Say No Campaign, 16

## K
Kosovo, 50
Kostunica, Vojislav, 50
Kuwait, 30, 31

## L
Lebanon, 17, 19
leukemia, 24, 29
Lewinsky, Monica, 44, 45, 47
liberal, 25, 28
Libya, 19
literacy, 28, 29

## M
Medicare, 41, 42
middle class, 8, 9
Milosevic, Slobodan, 50
minimum wage, 38
Ministers' Leadership Conference, 49, 52

## N
National Guard, 32
New World Order, 30, 54
Nicaragua, 19
Nixon, Richard, 14, 25, 33, 59, 61
Nobel Peace Prize, 39
Noriega, Manuel, 30
North Atlantic Treaty Organization, 50
North, Oliver, 20

# Presidents of the United States

# Index

Northern Ireland, 42
nuclear arms control, 20
nuclear power industry, 7

## O

Obama, Barack, 53, 59, 61
obstruction of justice, 45, 46, 47, 48, 49
O'Connor, Sandra Day, 16, 59
Oklahoma City, 9, 59
Olympic games (1996), 9
Operation Desert Storm, 31

## P

Palestine, 51
Panama, 30, 58
perjury, 45, 46, 48, 49
Persian Gulf, 31, 59
Powell, Colin, 31
protestors, 50

## Q

Qaddafi, Muammar al, 19
Quayle, J. Danforth, 22, 27, 32, 55

## R

Rainbow Coalition, 27
Reagan, Nancy, 4, 13, 15, 16, 21, 27
Reagan, Ronald, 3, 4, 10-21, 26, 27, 33, 47, 54, 59, 61
   born, 10, 12, 61
   died, 10, 21, 61
   First Lady, 10, 16
   term, 10, 61
   vice president, 10, 14, 19, 26
Reaganomics, 17
Rehnquist, William, 48
Roosevelt, Theodore, 52, 58, 61

## S

sanctions, 30, 31
Saudi Arabia, 30, 31
savings and loan, 44
savings and loan institutions, 17, 28, 44
Schwarzkopf, Norman, 31
Screen Actor's Guild, 13

Social Security, 41
Somalia, 37, 59
Soviet Union, 18, 20, 30, 59
Star Wars, 18
Starr, Kenneth, 38, 39, 43, 44, 45, 46, 47
Strategic Defense Initiative, 18
strike, 16, 42
Sudan, 42
supply-side economics, 17

## T

Teflon President, 54
terrorism, 9, 19, 59
trickle-down economics, 17
Tripp, Linda, 44

## U

U.S. Embassy, 14, 59
unemployment, 14, 40
United Nations inspectors, 42

## V

video culture, 6
Voodoo economics, 26

## W

weapons of mass destruction, 42
welfare aid, 38
Whitewater, 38, 44, 47
World Trade Organization, 50
World Trade Center, 9, 59
World War II, 13, 24, 30, 58

## Y

Yugoslavia, 50
yuppies, 4

# Further Reading

Amoroso, Cynthia. *Ronald Reagan*. The Childs World Inc., 2008.

Bausum, Ann. *Our Country's Presidents: All You Need to Know about the Presidents, from George Washington to Barack Obama*. National Geographic Society, 2009.

Barber, James David. *Eyewitness Presidents*. DK Publishing, Inc., 2008.

Hammond. *Hammond's Book of the Presidents*. Hammond World Atlas Corporation, 2009.

McPherson, Stephanie Sammartino. *Bill Clinton*. Lerner Publishing Group, 2008.

Paul, Mason. *Iraq*. Marshall Cavendish Inc., 2008.

Rubel, David. *Encyclopedia of the Presidents and Their Times*. Scholastic, Inc., 2009.

Welch, Catherine A. *George H.W. Bush*. Lerner Publishing Group, 2008.

# Websites to Visit

www.enchantedlearning.com/history/us/pres/list.shtml

www.whitehouse.gov/kids

http://pbskids.org/wayback/

www.kidinfo.com/American_History/Presidents.html